Haywain

Haywains & Cherry Ale

Also by Joan Kent

Binder Twine & Rabbit Stew
Lamplight on Cottage Loaves
Woodsmoke & Pigeon Pie

HAYWAINS & CHERRY ALE

Joan Kent

Century · London

First published 1980
Copyright © Joan Kent 1980

First published in the United Kingdom in 1980 by
Bailey Brothers and Swinfen Ltd

First published by Century Ltd in 1996
Random House, 20 Vauxhall Bridge Road, London SW1V 2SA

Random House Australia (Pty) Limited
20 Alfred Street, Milsons Point, Sydney,
New South Wales 2061, Australia

Random House New Zealand Limited
18 Poland Road, Glenfield
Auckland 10, New Zealand

Random House South Africa (Pty) Limited
PO Box 337, Bergvlei, South Africa

Random House UK Limited Reg. No. 954009
ISBN 0 7126 76481

Papers used by Random House UK Ltd are natural, recyclable
products made from wood grown in sustainable forests. The
manufacturing processes conform to the environmental
regulations of the country of origin.

Phototypeset by Intype London Ltd

Printed & bound in Great Britain by Mackays of Chatham PLC,
Chatham, Kent

Contents

To Alan, the blacksmith's eldest son.
With love.

Introduction

When I found a skein of green beads beneath the torn lining of a woven work basket Mum had bought for next to nothing at an auction sale, she dismissed them as a paltry bonus, for fancy jewellery had no place in her hard working life. I, her afterthought, the youngest of her nine children, was a compulsive traveller on flights of fancy, a persistent weaver of dreams wherein the necklace sparkling like raindrops on beech leaves bursting from their buds in springtime, provided the means of solving my parents' farming and financial problems, making us all extremely rich.

I sometimes disentangled the string of beads from unwound cotton bobbins, buttons, lengths of elastic, darning wool and stay laces that conglomerated in a treacherous tangle. Making sure that they were safely hidden from sight, I wore the beads to school, certain that I was the only pupil sitting in that draughty village schoolroom with a string of fabulously precious gems hung around my neck.

Inevitably the fraying thread parted company with the clasp as I hurried home across the meadows at the end of the day's lessons. Many of the scattered beads were lost in the long grass. Those I retrieved were put into a gaudy vase that held a multitude of hat pins, awaiting the time when Mum could find thread fine and strong enough for the skein to be restrung.

By the time that happened, the top heavy vase had been tipped over so often that many more beads had disappeared. My left-handed attempt to restore the necklace produced a loose string lacking sequence, and too short to fasten around anyone's neck. They remained in the 'oddments' drawer of the front room table for years on end with no one questioning their value or establishing their worth.

When the new brooms of a changing, post war era brushed aside all that my parents had strived for in their life span, the string of green beads was just another broken link that was swept away.

I experienced too many hard winters to harbour any illusion of that vanished country world being a rural Arcadia, yet there was always laughter bubbling just beneath the surface; a great sense of purpose, pride, and wellbeing abounding in the timeless beauty of that slower, smaller sphere. One learned to differentiate between riches and true worth.

So the skein will never be complete again, for so much was lost, with no one questioning the losing.

Just as once I tried to rethread a broken skein of beads, so in this my third book, have I attempted to restring with clumsy fingers, small cameos of times remembered, knowing that only the fickle thread of fraying memory prevents them from being lost in the long grass.

JOAN KENT
BEAM ENDS

viii

The Shearing of Sister Eve

I had five older sisters who would chatter like sparrows round an unthatched oat stack, but they always closed their adult ranks and changed the subject whenever I asked the plain and simple question:

"How will I know when I have grown up?"

I thought I had found some useful information when I scanned through some pages of *Poppy's Weekly Paper* that had come home wrapped round our Friday herrings. It said that no youthful person could hope to become a real young lady until she put her hair up neatly, remembering always to wear a hat when she went out. To illustrate the point, there were photographs of several smartly elegant females wearing magnificently decorated millinery that was anchored by enormous hat pins on either side of their heads.

Growing like a small cloud on my mind's horizon, a preposterous suspicion began to take shape in my brain. A vase on the front room overmantel shelf seemed to confirm my fears. It was crammed with hat pins of every length and colour, from small gilt ones to lethal-looking weapons ornamented with gob-stopper-sized 'jewels'.

These began to hold a terrifying fascination, making me so apprehensive that I kept taking surreptitious glances in the damp-speckled overmantel mirror, convinced that I had discovered the process by which one changed from a child into an adult girl. I searched anxiously for the first signs and symptoms of having 'hat pin holes' develop just above my ears on each side of my head. I knew that Mum had pierced ears, and wondered if one underwent some secret similar operation, or if they appeared suddenly, like holes in worn out socks.

It became an obsessive interest to watch Mum and my sisters anchoring their hats to their long hair with a gaudy assortment of hat pins that were prodded into one side of their craniums, and emerged on the opposite side. Hat pin holes could well explain why Mum always wore her hair swept up onto the top of her head in a top-knot bun. This style probably kept out draughts and helped prevent her catching colds in the head. It would also explain why I alone still had my hair washed in the Saturday bathtub, while my sisters indulged in the luxury of their Friday night shampoos.

It was understandable now that I could endure enamel jugs of rinsing water being poured over my unperforated head, but with hat pin holes to contend with such drastic treatment might well waterlog my sisters' brains. No wonder Friday evenings were such a ritual of boiled rainwater and vinegar rinsings. Lorelei, circa nineteen thirty, they sat round the fire drying their long tresses, showing their short sleeved cotton vests, their camisoles and lace edged petticoats. Curling tongs cooled on the fender, steel toothed 'rat trap' wavers were tightly clamped to encourage corrugated ridges in their hair. Home made setting lotion, owing much to corn starch, was scented with 'Ashes Of Roses' to hide the homely plain-Jane smell of soft soap shampoo.

Dad bought soft soap by the barrel because it had several veterinary uses. As a shampoo it gave our hair a shining sheen like the coat of a well-groomed horse. Dad was inordinately proud of his daughters' long tresses, leaving no one in doubt as

to his disappointment and displeasure if any of them was daft
enough to take notice of the latest craze and attempt to have it
cut.

Shop-bought make up was considered to be sheer extravagance, daring if not decadent, but *Zebra* black lead stove polish
served to accentuate line of brow, or length of eye lash, while
petals from the red geraniums on the kitchen window were
sometimes pressed into colouring my sisters' cheeks and lips. It
puzzled Mum why her prized pot plants always showed such
budding promise, but produced such tatty blooms. Not made to
go to bed as long as I kept quiet and turned the phonograph
handle as required, I watched the world of grown-ups from
behind the barrier of being 'small'; a world I had become convinced that I would need hat pin holes to join. This did not
appeal to me at all.

Our old phonograph was so worn with use that it sometimes
developed hiccoughs, but we never tired of the cylindrical
records that it played. We sang along with Enrico Caruso, Lily
Morris, Dame Nellie Melba, Count John McCormack. Florrie
Ford, Nellie Wallace and the rest. At that time my sister Eve
worked in the city and could purchase records at a discount.
These were added to the dozens already stacked up among Mum's
wine and cherry ale brews in the huge old cupboard known as
'the glory hole'.

My strait-laced Aunt Florence was staying with us when Eve
brought home the record of a new dance that a dashing young
electrician had shown her. The phonograph churned out the
music of The Charleston until it faltered from the strain. In
trying to keep the rhythm going until her sisters had mastered
the new technique of dancing. Eve leaned over the phonograph,
catching her long hair in the machinery of the roller. With yards
of hair wound into its entrails, the phonograph slurred to a stop.
Held fast, her head within inches of the machine, Eve had to
be hacked free with Mum's dressmaking scissors. She looked like
a badly sheared sheep that had escaped half way through the
operation, so the only solution was to cut the rest of her hair
off short.

Eve was delighted, for who could dance the Black Bottom or
The Charleston, shedding hair pins as they went. Dad's displeasure was muted by the fact that Mum had done the shearing,

but he maintained that short hair made Eve look like the back view of a bob-tailed old sheepdog. I was scared to look too closely, worrying that Eve's hat pin holes would now be exposed and let in the rain.

Watching the phonograph being jammed into eternal silence, Aunt Flo expressed the belief that this was divine retribution for the sinful music it had been made to play. The sight of my sisters 'cavorting like pagans' had made her expect some more wrathful form of judgement to descend on our old farmhouse like a thunderbolt from the sky. Looking at Eve's shorn head, my aunt rooted around in Mum's workbasket and got busy knitting a huge shapeless 'tammy' hat that could cover the wanton shamelessness of Eve's naked neck.

"Will it be good and thick enough to cover her ears and keep the wet out?" I asked as I watched Aunt's needles flying. Bolt upright in her iron maiden corsets that forbade any slouching, she glared at me, saying:

"If you've no more sense than to pester a person counting stitches, you can take yourself off and worry your Dad.'

Fraught with anxiety about the situation, this I did. He assured me that my fears about hat pin holes were completely groundless, but admitted that he had often wondered how women managed to use such vicious looking weapons to anchor their hats. He knew that none of the females in our family had leaky craniums, so I had no need to worry on that score. Even if the worst of my fears became reality, he reminded me about the gaping hole in the cart shed roof that he had mended with felt and pitch. Short haired, or still retaining their 'crowning glory', all his daughters were quite safe. As for knowing when I had reached the stage of being grown up, Dad reckoned it to be more of an attitude of mind than birthdays.

"Jo," he said. "There are some folk who were born old. Your Aunt Flo never seemed young and carefree. She was probably weaned on crab apples. You can be young at heart if you are ninety, so just you stay as you are for as long as you can."

A great weight lifted from my heart as I went back into the lamplit kitchen where Aunt's disapproval hung in the atmosphere like a grey, wet blanket and everyone seemed subdued. I had seen Mum looking happier in the middle of a wet washing day. She suggested we might please Aunt Flo and occupy ourselves by making music of our own. But none of my sisters had progressed far beyond playing 'A Maiden's Prayer' on the front room piano.

Instead they sat round the kitchen table making felt cloche hats, or attempting to disguise the fact that they were shortening their skirts to a more fashionable length. Sitting on the broken-springed old sofa under the window, Stan tried his hand at learning the ukelele in ten easy lessons, making little progress because his finances did not run to buying the actual instrument, but only the manual of instructions, and even that was second hand. Billy, the quietest, most serious-minded of my brothers, was so engrossed in the book he was reading that he was oblivious to everything else. Harold was trying to drum up enthusiasm for his idea that making a crystal wireless set was not beyond his capabilities, but our censorious aunt disapproved most strongly, remarking that anyone dabbling with dark forces would be sorry.

For once, I was glad to be youngest, first to leave the dismal, alien atmosphere of our kitchen and go to bed. Offering consolation as she came upstairs to take away my candle. Mum said that Aunt Flo would only stay a few days more. The reason for her visit was an auction sale in a nearby country mansion, where she hoped to find some 'bargain lots'. A real gramophone that played flat records instead of round ones was listed in the catalogue of the sale, and providing that we all promised not to antagonise our crusty visitor. Mum said she would try to buy it. We spent the next few days acting like ministering cherubs.

"There, Liza!" Aunt Flo crowed. "You can see now that you would have a fairly presentable family if you were not as soft as butter! See what wise words and firm handling can do!"

When Stan drove the horse and cart to fetch Mum and Aunt Flo from the auction sale. I rode with him and helped him stack their trophies in the cart. Stan brought out a Hudson's Soap box packed with flat records, then carefully placed a small mahogany cabinet beside it. Next came a huge tin horn that looked like a green convolvulus blossom. I was warned to guard it carefully, and the safest way I could think of was to ride back wearing it like a pixie hat wedged on my head.

By lamplight that evening. Harold put the mahogany cabinet on the red velvet table cloth, then carefully secured a steel needle in the sound reproducing box. He wound the handle and

started the turntable, while we all sat awe-struck at the volume
of noise that could come from a green tin horn.

Since the instrument had been owned by 'gentry', the second
hand records ranged from light classical to downright heavy.
These were not what any of Mum's family would have chosen,
but we sat and listened, for they seemed to give her a new
dimension to living, offering an entrancing, instant escape from
her humdrum hard-working world.

Various fiancés, girl friends, and 'intendeds' swelled our ranks
that evening. Eve had used all her Friday wages to have her hair
properly shingled and buy some flat records of her own choice.
Short haired and thoroughly modern, she entertained us by
singing. "You called me baby doll a year ago, boopy-doop, boopy-
doop." she carolled, quick-stepping round the kitchen with her
low-waisted, short frock showing bare leg above flesh-coloured
stockings held up with garters sporting bold embroidery and blue
silk bows. Skeins of beads swung defiantly around her throat,
marking the beat of the music as she danced.

Aunt Flo watched this display in stupified silence, then rose
majestically to prod the sound box of the gramophone with her
knitting needle as if it was some foul pest. The needle scratched
across the record, repeated a couple of phrases, then stopped.

"Shameless wanton!" Aunt declaimed. "Just suppose that you
were 'took' this instant – and you should be – you would be cast
into the everlasting pit like the whore of Babylon! Think on
that!"

Dad said firmly that there would be no more of that kind of
talk in this house, so Aunt adopted the attitude of an over-
worked avenging angel returning from a particularly arduous
earthly assignment to find the gates of Heaven slammed shut.

Mum tried to smooth ruffled feelings by suggesting that we
listen to a boy soprano singing 'Jerusalem', but she picked up
the wrong record in her confusion. Aunt Flo looked as if she
had been mentally pole-axed as Marie Lloyd belted out the
chorus of 'A Little Of What You Fancy Does You Good'. She
stood stock-still for a second, then deliberately sat down on a
pile of records Mum had placed on a nearby chair. There was
an ominous crack beneath her and, rising slowly, she turned to
inspect the damage, saying:

"Dear me! I seem to have sat in your 'Monastery Garden' Liza, and me a strict noncomformist too!"

Mum quietly picked up the broken pieces, then closed the gramophone lid. We all knew that it would stay shut until our prickly aunt went home. This decision came quite suddenly the following morning. Harold eagerly agreed to load all her luggage and sale bargains in the tip cart, then drive her to her pristine city home. Waving a somewhat relieved farewell as she watched Aunt departing down the farm lane. Mum told us why.

"I just mentioned that I felt really slovenly because everyone else who takes pride in their home has finished spring cleaning, and I haven't begun. Nor has Flo for that matter," said my mother guilelessly, "but now she's hurried home to put that right!"

Dad took her in his arms, lifting her off her feet to hug her, the pair of them giggling all the while. I knew then that growing up had nothing to do with hat pins. My parents could still laugh like children. I would be the same, and stay young all my life.

Welcome, Stranger

We accepted that, during the lengthening days when hares go mad, Mum's rites of spring transformed her to a cottage-loaf-shaped Nemesis, stirring up the contents of the house from attic to doorstep. Eiderdowns, rugs, feather beds, pillows, and blankets were likely to be pitched out of upper windows, to be beaten or brushed to death in the yard below. For the last few years however, Mum's routine of spring cleaning had been thoroughly disorganised by the fact that there was a sudden spate of family weddings.

Each one was an excuse to scrub and shine anything with a solid surface, shake and thump that which was moveable but unlaunderable, and use tubs full of soap suds to drown anything that would wash.

Soon after my twelfth birthday, we were subjected to a particularly violent recurrence, but this time the driving force was my sister June. By then June and Nora were the only two sisters left unmarried. Mum's three youngest daughters were known as 'the pretty one', 'the stylish brainy one' and 'that skinny little one with the ears!'

June suddenly became so houseproud that Mum could only offer the illogical explanation that the girl must be in love. Being blessed with so many brothers and sisters, romance was a phenomenon I had often witnessed, but it had never before inspired any of them to re-arrange the kitchen or attempt to persuade the rest of us that meals would taste much better if we ate them in the cold front room, June had either been bitten by a very virulent love bug, or there was something extraordinary about her young man.

It transpired that, while all the rest had chosen life partners from within the county boundaries, June was being courted by a civil servant, an unknown species, alien to our way of life. Dad was apprehensive, wondering if his daughter intended bringing home one of the brainless, nosy individuals who sat on their backsides in Ministry offices dreaming up stupid forms demanding information on everything on the farm right down to the last hogget, shearling, and one-toothed gimmer. He made it clear from the outset that his welcome would be luke-warm. June's intimation that her young man was attached to the Indian Civil Service did nothing to help matters. She took down the bobbled fringe drape from around the shelf above the fire place, saying that it was old-fashioned. A string line hidden beneath it had always been used for warming and airing our clothes, but we were all expected to make sacrifices in the cause of June's new love.

Everything cluttering the mantel shelf was ruthlessly cleared. The paper spills for Dad's pipe, bills, receipts, and a strange shaped fossil Stan once found in the brook. Even the vase of hat pins was banished to the dark depths of a cupboard.

June did her best to give the place such a stately image that it did not feel like home at all. I even earned the unbelievably large wage of one shilling and sixpence for colour-washing the interior of our 'outback' privy, a glorious salmon pink. Applied with enthusiasm, this trickled through the cracks of the lap-boarded walls, overlaying the tarred exterior with irregular pink stripes which I considered helped to brighten up that particular aspect of the garden immensely, but no-one else shared my view. Nor was my finishing touch of 'quick drying' mahogany stain varnish appreciated. The label illustration showed an overalled painter clutching a shaft of forked lightning in front of him, the motto of the produce being 'It dries in a flash.'

Bitter experience showed that it didn't. The seat of the 'outback' proved an embarrassingly sticky hazard with no hope of impressing our expected visitor, when a bottle of white spirit, clean rag, and a small mirror were vital impedimenta kept in constant readiness on the 'outback' shelf.

June worked in the city all week, so Sunday was the day chosen for her young man's initial visit. This allowed as many as possible of our relations to inspect the rare specimen June had caught.

I had a hastily sewn new white dress for the occasion and my usually plaited hair was twisted and turned into scalp-torturing curling rag knots, to emerge as a shock headed frizz.

June went to meet her sweetheart in a state of nervous apprehension as various aunts, uncles and cousins arrived. Flushed and flustered in the kitchen, Mum stood basting a large hunk of sheep. It took up so much room in the oven that there was scarcely room to roast the potatoes, so our dessert had to be something that would cook on top of the stove. Mum settled for her version of fig pudding.

'Figgy Duff' consisted of flour, lumpy suet, brown sugar, dried figs and as much milk as it took to bind the ingredients together in a cloth. This boiled and chuntered away, needing but cursory attention, giving Mum the opportunity to meet June and her escort on his arrival, then dart back to the kitchen and compare opinions with Dad.

The young man was frightfully 'upper crust', striding around in brown and white shoes and loud checked socks matching the pattern of his tweed plus-fours. Speaking with a strange accent, he called Dad 'Sir', but this cut no ice with my father. If Mum wanted his opinion, yonder chap was nought but a fly-by-night bird catcher, with no more chance of getting his permission to take June off to India than anyone else had of ever walking on the moon.

"I can't understand the girl!" he remarked glumly. "She should have the sense not to get lumbered with stock lacking good teeth, no matter if it has got a good bloom to its coat."

Alternately stirring gravy and custard, I felt a pang of disillusion. The dashing young man's gleaming white smile had reminded me of Douglas Fairbanks, but there seemed little romance in the thought of June watching him remove his dentures each night. Mum's only comment was that she was glad she had chosen 'Figgy Duff' as afters. She smiled gleefully as it expanded to lift the lid of the old two-handled iron pot.

Nora had set the front room table, adding a centrepiece posy of flowers as an artistic touch. Aunt Flo, who would not have missed so interesting an encounter for all the tea in China, deplored the sinful waste of roses and madonna lilies that might have made a lovely wreath.

The first course of that Sunday lunch was eaten in disconcerting silence, with most of us anxious to use our knives and forks correctly although the specially polished cutlery left a metallic taste in our mouths.

As I carried empty plates to the kitchen, I found Mum facing the problem of a Figgy Duff that had expanded to such an extent that she could not remove it from the pot. I thought that removing the water around it might make it more amenable, but our kitchen lacked such modernities as sink or waste pipes so, each holding a handle, we carried the heavy oval iron pot out to the 'sump', a shallow indentation in the back garden, where the slightest shower of rain made a tiny trickling streamlet saunter through.

Prodding, shaking, and tilting, Mum tried to manoeuvre the pudding from its iron prison. One desperate tug on the pudding cloth made it fall 'ker-plop' into the almost stagnant green water. Mum grabbed at it, then used her apron to wipe off the worst of the slimy water weed.

She surveyed it in silence for a moment, then solemnly remarked:

"It doesn't appear to have lost anything. No one will notice a drop of sump water if we cover it in custard. What won't fatten will fill!"

I pleaded loss of appetite, watching the others eating their Figgy Duff with relish. There was, however, one exception. June's admirer removed a stray blade of grass to the side of his plate, then took a tentative mouthful but seemed loath to chew. Instantly my parents began bombarding him with questions: Was the pudding to his liking? Had he hunted tigers? What was the price of wheat in Baluchistan?

As befitting a mainstay of the British Raj, he tried manfully to answer, but his conversation dried up under the torture of fig seeds between his dentures and his gums.

Mum detailed me to spend the afternoon keeping close to June and her young man wherever they might wander. Mo, my cousin, volunteered to accompany me. We were much the same age and he shared my interest in collecting cigarette cards and climbing trees.

The pretence that we were Red Indians stalking two white settlers across the prairie soon became boring because the young man would keep stopping to kiss June's ears. When the pair of them had sat on the same stile holding hands for over an hour, Mo and I decided to go sailing in sheep troughs on the pond in Church Field. Mine sank, ruining my new dress with the same green weedy water that had clung to Mum's Figgy Duff.

Mum seemed less bothered by my ducking than by my dereliction of family duty. She explained the implications of June marrying the smooth-talking gentleman who had damned all his chances with Dad by acting as if he was granting June a great honour by considering the possibility of making her his wife.

"Do you want her to sail off to India, that red blob on the other side of the globe and become a memsahib?" Mum asked with some urgency. I did not. Before my brother Billy left home, I had found one of his paperback novels in his bedroom cupboard and had a crafty read of the contents before Mum used it as 'ammunition' in the outback. The title of that epic was *The Memsahib Slave*, and it dealt with the traumatic adventures of a poor young lady constantly being pursued and captured by a Rajah. The front cover illustrated a huge, coloured gentleman towering above a crouching fair-haired female, draped in what appeared to me to be white lace curtains. In no way did I want my beautiful sister June to go to a place where girls dressed as scantily as that.

I discussed the situation with my cousin, but Mo was as bereft of ideas as myself. Watching June's young man slipping down the garden path to the outback, Mo thought he should be warned about the mahogany varnish but I called him back. A few seconds later we strolled down the garden path to feed the rabbit in its hutch by the privy, nonchalantly chatting as we walked. I said loudly that Mum was sure that a nice sea cruise to India would do wonders for June's attacks of the screaming hysterics, and might even reduce them to less than one a week.

Mo asked if being in love had stopped her heavy drinking.

Just for good measure we threw in some garbled yarn about Dad's hopes that a wealthy new son-in-law might save the family farm from the bailiffs. With an inspired stroke of perfidious genius, we added ten years to June's real age.

As June's swain emerged from the outback, still wiping his hands on the turps rag, we acted out our guilty embarrassment, expressing the loud and fervent hope that he had not overheard our conversation because Dad would be furious if another of June's catches slipped the hook. The disillusioned Romeo feigned sickness, departing at tea time, and Mum's Figgy Duff was blamed.

Nora took June into the front room to cry in privacy and comfort. I could hear them trying to play duets on the piano and singing weepy songs of unrequited love. June's grief lasted for at least a fortnight, then she met up with a smart young man in the city's Silver Band. Dad proposed that she brought this one home for inspection quickly because another bout of refurbishing, privy varnishing, and never knowing where his boots, pipe lighters, or working jacket were likely to be hidden, was more than a tolerant chap like him could stand.

The Five Legged Rabbit

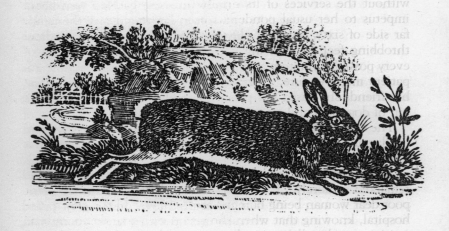

Thirza Kittle seldom encountered any sort of traffic as she plodded through the quiet lanes on her weekly shopping expeditions, so the excitement of hearing the warning bell of the town ambulance ringing ever closer made her risk life, limb, and her best lisle stockings to scramble up in the thorny hedgerow to watch the box-sided vehicle approach.

As it slowly progressed along the roughly surfaced track, she was able to peer through the sepia tinted side window long enough to identify the patient on the stretcher in the back. This confirmed a local 'confidential' rumour that the village nurse had been taken so sadly that she might well require major surgery for some unmentionable female complaint.

In a parish so placidly peaceful that two dogs fighting constituted a major excitement, the village shop was the social centre, a meeting place where Thirza could chat with her cronies, spicing mundane grocery shopping with a sprinkling of local gossip and companionship each Friday afternoon. The fact that a quarter-mile-long farm track separated Thirza from her nearest neighbour never prevented her from finding the most intriguing and interesting snippets of information to mull over with her friends.

Her anxiety to break the news that the community would be without the services of its ministering angel added speed and impetus to her usual ponderous pace. Overweight and on the far side of sixty, hurrying played havoc with her puffy legs and throbbing feet but, having occupied her mind by thinking of every possible symptom and complication that the nurse-turned-patient might endure, Thirza limped into the shop. Pushing past her friends she eased her perspiring bulk up on to the top of a bin of dog meal and sat panting, trying to regain her breath.

The state of Thirza's lower extremities had often provided fuel for flagging conversations, but on this particular occasion it was a subject she was not keen to pursue.

"It ain't my poor old feet that makes my heart bleed!" she remarked sombrely. "It sets me off of a shake to think of that poor dear woman being bumped and bounced all the way to the hospital, knowing that when she gets there some doctor will be waiting to take all her insides away! How are the rest of us to manage should we get struck down sudden, with no trained help at hand?"

Seeing that the perplexed shoppers looked suitably awestruck, Thirza leaned forward, brushing aside a dusty dangling flypaper that had long since lured its last victim to a gum-stuck death.

Straightening a wide-brimmed straw hat that drooped over her ears like a cosy covering the spout and handle of a tea pot, she paused to heighten the dramatic effect.

"And what about our weekly descriptions?" she continued. "Will we still be covered? Can anyone answer that?"

"Descriptions?" The shopkeeper looked as nonplussed as her customers.

"Ah!" said Thirza. "And well might you ask! You pays your penny a week into the Country Nursing Fund box the same as the rest of us, but do you think we're likely to get a halfpenny piece in change while we're without a nurse?"

Within minutes every anatomical detail of the nurse's ailment had been discussed, then the subject veered to the effect her absence would have on those village women who were in 'the family way' and near their time. The assembled shoppers could think of only one such case facing this predicament, and then the patient was unlikely to have problems. With eleven children already, it was the Friday shoppers' considered opinion that 'Slap-Cabbage Sal' would find her twelfth confinement as simple as a sun-dried broom seed popping from the pod.

Thirza kept her own counsel on that particular subject. Sal might be a 'slap-cabbage' slattern, wed to a leery, loutish, work-shy husband, but she was cousin to Thirza's late husband and therefore a relative of sorts. Skilfully changing the subject, she suggested that the most urgent problem was likely to be old Grandad Walls, should the weather turn nasty and bring on one of his bronchial spells again.

Sadie Walls, the old man's daughter-in-law and a Friday regular, agreed that when it came to applying a kaolin poultice to his chest, the district nurse was the only female that the cantankerous old curmudgeon would trust to lift his nightshirt higher than his knees. Sadie hoped that nurses from adjoining areas might keep an eye on the village or a temporary replacement nurse might be sent to help out.

By virtue of the fact that Thirza's nephew was courting a kitchen helper at the town cottage hospital, she was believed to have access to information denied others. The rest looked at her expectantly.

"Ah!" she said enigmatically. "We shall have to wait and see!"

At the next Friday shopping session, Thirza offered a graphic description of a surgeon's stitchcraft that had made the nurse-turned-patient's stomach resemble an embroidered patchwork cushion. This did not make the dramatic impact she considered it to deserve. It seemed that everyone else had seen, heard, or met the new nurse who had arrived in the village without her knowing, but this fact Thirza tried to keep to herself.

The others looked incredulous as she admitted, "I can't say I've noticed her about."

"Once seen never forgotten!" the shopkeeper retorted. "You must have heard her roaring around the place on that noisy motorbike."

The thought of a nurse straddling one of those fearsome, smelly objects seemed to Thirza to be downright unladylike, undignified and vaguely indecent.

"Well, her certainly don't ride it side-saddle, Thirza." Tilly Hackett giggled, elbowing the other Friday regulars within nudging distance. "She was over at Grandad Walls' place as I came across the green. If we keep an eye and ear open for her leaving, then you can judge for yourself." Thinking aloud as the motor cyclist stopped outside the village store, Thirza was sure that in all her days she had never seen an apparition like the tall, broad-shouldered figure in knee boots, cavalry riding breeches, leather gauntlets, blue melton cloth donkey jacket and a gaberdine nursing uniform hat.

"If you want my honest opinion," Thirza said earnestly, "There's a bit of jiggerypokery going on somewhere. That's no nursing sister! They're trying to palm us off with some weirdy kind of chap."

Standing six feet tall in her studded boots, the nurse strode into the shop, and not knowing that shopping was an afternoon-long session for the Friday regulars, said she would take her turn in the queue. Unanimous in agreement that the nature of her work gave her top priority, the cronies watched with interest to see what she would buy.

"Five dozen dust combs, bug rakes, nit crackers, or whatever you like to call them," boomed the nurse, more baritone than contralto.

A couple of small-toothed combs, discoloured on a card, had hung unsold in the shop for so long that the price mark had faded completely. The prospect of selling five whole cards at one go made the shopkeeper check that she had heard aright.

"That's it!" The nurse re-affirmed. "Sixty will ensure that each pupil at the village school can be checked at home. I'm damned if I like having to hack off a child's hair because its head is crawling with lice!"

Taking this as a slur on the local women, the lady shoppers protested that there were only one or two suspect families in the parish. The rest were scrupulously clean. "They are the poor blighters that get infected by the others! I plan to eliminate the infestation at the school if I have to kill lice singly by stamping on them with my fairy feet!" The nurse spoke cheerfully, her laughter rumbling like the echoing tide in some deep cliff-face cavern. "Incidentally, can anyone direct me to a Mrs. Thirza Kittle's house?" Thirza made herself known and, as the nurse asked her to step outside for a moment, speculation among the other Friday shoppers ran riot.

The nurse's main preoccupation was with nursing the sick, killing nits, or delivering babies. Thirza was so healthy and wholesome that she was unlikely to be troubled by the first two contingencies, she was also far too long in the tooth to be involved in the third.

When Thirza returned to her shopping, she was extremely subdued, dismissing her chat as being just a bit of friendly consultation, but venturing the opinion that under the nurse's mannish, hearty exterior, was a thoughtful soul with a heart to match her size.

The truth was that on her ante-natal visit to 'Slap-Cabbage Sal', the nurse had taken one look at the horde of lethargic, ill-nourished children swarming amid the squalor and knew that she must find some good-hearted soul to offer her mistreated, thoroughly defeated patient a helping hand.

Enquiries had shown Thirza to be remotely connected with this problem case, so the nurse could only prevail on the tenuous 'cousin by marriage' link and rely on the humanity of this good hearted, if garrulous soul.

Thirza realised that her cronies were not satisfied with her brief explanation, but family shame for the pigsty conditons surrounding Sal's imminent confinement called for prevarication. She told them she had consented to do some voluntary assistant nursing, providing her poor old feet would stand the strain. She then maintained the discreet silence demanded by medical ethics and let her friends ruminate over that.

On the day Sal's twelfth child made up its mind to start arriving, the nurse rode over for Thirza in a hurry. Perilously perched on the pillion of the twin-engined 'Brough Superior' motor cycle, Thirza was convinced that she would die of fright if her lights and liver were not jolted and jarred to atoms, but had to admit that covering the mile and a quarter journey in two minutes was a lot easier on her throbbing feet. Any discomforts of the journey were soon forgotten as she hobbled over the threshold of Sal's poverty-stricken home.

Thirza bustled around, stoking up the corner copper to boil water, coping with the children that swarmed under her feet like ants. Sal's labour was surprisingly long and protracted in the early stage, so the nurse donned a sackcloth scrubbing apron and set to helping Thirza clean house. They even managed to launder a load of bed linen, and by evening a hovel with all the charm of a rubbish dump became a reasonably presentable place.

As Thirza and the nurse sat waiting for Sal's contractions to increase in intensity. Thirza remarked that although she had no personal experience of childbirth, it seemed to cause Sal less discomfort than she was personally suffering with her feet.

"Let me take a look at them, Thirza!" Friendly as it was, the nurse's voice brooked no argument. Thirza rolled down her stockings to reveal a pair of feet that her overweight state had prevented her from reaching down to tend for years. Before she could object they were soaking in a pan of hot soda water, while one of the round-eyed, runny-nosed small spectators watching this exceptional operation was dispatched to the village black-smith for the loan of the kind of iron rasp the farrier used to file down the horses' hooves.

The nurse needed all her strength to prune back the calcified ingrown nails that had been so long untended that they had extended over the top of each tortured toe. Thirza did far more groaning than the woman in labour, and when the baby suddenly arrived just as the nurse finished filing Thirza's tenth toenail, there were three patients, all bawling with relief.

Feeling nimble as a young filly, Thirza trotted around looking after Sal and her brood, but found time to collect her weekly Friday groceries the next afternoon. To the other shoppers eagerly awaiting a grunt-by-grunt account of Sal's confinement, she announced that a miracle worker had come among them.

"There she was," she enthused, "calm as you please, curing my poor crippled old paddlers and delivering soft headed Sal's little one all in a matter of moment, with no fuss or commotion. That's what I call a proper nurse."

The shopkeeper suggested that it might be more useful if the nurse could cure Sal's loutish husband of his drunken depraved habits, for he had been caught acting like an old tom cat with a servant up at The Hall according to some. If the nurse could work a miracle or two in his direction there would be fewer drunken brawls, black eyes, or babies for 'Slap-Cabbage Sal', and a good-hearted soul like Thirza would not be traipsing back and forth to clean up a midden or mind a parcel of kids. If Thirza was expected to make an answer, the assembled women were disappointed. She had never been one to stand idly by when folk around her were in trouble and, while she personally favoured castration for Sal's husband, she kept her opinion to herself.

Another Friday shopper, Tilly Hackett, filled the awkward silence that followed with the comment:

"My Tom's old mother wouldn't agree that the nurse is an angel, Thirza! She's up at Foxley End chuntering something chronic, calling her a ham-hoofed cart horse and suchlike. For my part, I ain't much of a praying woman, but I tell you straight that for this last few days I've given thanks on my knees that this new nurse came!"

Glad to have the focus of attention taken from her own disreputable relatives. Thirza urged Tilly to explain. As everyone knew, Mrs. Hackett senior always took her bad back to bed at the first cold twinge of winter every year. The previous nurse had popped in to give her 'creaking screwmatics' an occasional oiling with embrocation and Mrs. Hackett had stayed bedbound, suffering in comfort until spring. She considered it a small trifle to ask of her daughter-in-law that she tended fires, cooked, cleaned and cared for her when Tilly and Tom lived not more than a two mile step away.

Tom's mother had sent for the new nurse because an autumnal spell had driven her to bed. The nurse had shown less interest in the patient's carefully listed symptoms than in the sagging springs of the bed. She bounced the mattress up and down until the brass bedknobs rattled and, when Mrs. Hackett made groaning sounds appropriate to suppressed agony, diagnosed a classic hypothetical condition that needed drastic action right away. As she watched the nurse clump out of her bedroom, Mrs. Hackett snuggled under her coverlet and wondered what kind of treatment she might expect.

She had not heard the like of the bumping and thumping noises coming from downstairs since the village carpenter and undertaker had brought coffin boards up the narrow staircase on the night her husband died. It had been something of a shock to learn that she had an affliction that the nurse could put a name to, but it was disconcerting to think that the clod-hopper in a starched apron believed her to be as far gone as that. She was relieved to see the nurse re-enter the bedroom with the top board of her scullery trestle table, but when brawny arms that brooked no argument lifted her bodily from her bed to sit on the seat of her commode, she was not so sure.

Mrs. Hackett watched her precious goose feather bed being hauled into the damp back bedroom. The trestle boards were shoved beneath the hard, unyielding horse hair under-mattress, and within minutes she was tightly tucked into a pillow-less comfortless bed. Questioning the nature of her ailment and her treatment, she was told there was a simple alternative to staying where she was. The best remedy for her creaking joints was to give the house a clean and polish from top to bottom. Activity was the best cure the nurse could recommend.

Tilly Hackett related how she had arrived to find her mother-in-law up, dressed, and looking as joyful as a second-hand shroud. She confided that it was the 'High Patheticals' that ailed her, and while it was the modern treatment to make a poor tormented sufferer sleep on boards like a parish pauper, no navvy in a nursing apron would deny her the right to sleep on the feather mattress that had been a wedding present from her husband's grandmother, even if it meant gritting her teeth and bearing the burden of her illness by herself.

All Tilly knew was that for the first time since her marriage to Tom, she could look forward to a winter without rushing over to Foxley End in fair weather or foul, walking miles back and forth seven days a week. She reiterated her unstinting gratitude to the new nurse, but wondered how she had managed to cure Thirza's crippled feet, deliver 'Slap-Cabbage Sal's baby, and cope with eleven kids and all sorts of animals running in and out of the place.

Thirza realized she was being invited to make further comment on the intimate details of Sal's confinement, but the squalid misery of the woman was too painful to discuss.

In any case she could not linger for as long as usual because the nurse was taking her back to Sal's when the shopping session was done. And the first problem was evident as soon as Thirza and the nurse arrived there.

A bewildered, unweaned toddler was in his mother's bedroom, screaming to the full extent of his lungpower because every time he clambered on to her bed to nuzzle against her full breasts, he was pushed aside in favour of the new baby that had overnight usurped his place. A waif of a girl, Sal's oldest daughter, tried to pacify him by tying sugar in a snippet of rag like a miniature pudding, then popping the makeshift comforter into his open mouth.

When this failed to quieten him, she let him hold a wriggling rabbit she gently withdrew from above the waistband of her torn and buttonless dress. Frustrated in his infantile fury, wanting only comfort from his mother, the enraged toddler hurled it onto the woman's bed.

Sal shrieked like a soul tormented, terror contorting the features of her thin pale face. Covering her newborn babe with the bedclothes, she cuffed the rejected infant, then flung the rabbit toward her eldest daughter. It hit the wall behind her, landing on the floor to squirm spasmodically for a few moments before it was still. "You bloody stupid ninny, Lizzie. Ain't I got enough troubles without you deliberately wishing another load of misery on my shoulders? Take that devilish unnatural creature out of here or I'll get out of this bed and belt you, straight I will!"

Between sobs, the patient entreated the nurse to make sure the baby was not deformed or birth-scarred and, having ensured that the child was remarkably lusty, the puzzled nurse shooed all the rest of the family into the kitchen and bid her patient rest.

The eldest child sat on the hearthrug, rocking back and forth, crooning softly to the rabbit that lay lifeless in her arms, while Thirza made a start on ironing borrowed bed sheets.

"Get out from under my feet when I'm back and forth heating the flatiron Lizzie!" she said sharply. "For goodness sake take that outside and bury it, it's too scrawny to skin for your dinner. Why on earth did you have to upset your mother, with her in childbed. It's wishing misery on her. She's the last creature on God's earth to want an increase in family within the year! With eleven little brothers and sisters to play with, why did you cart around a thing like that?"

Lizzie's cowed, almost furtive expression made Thirza reassure her that no one was going to hit her, then the girl said quaveringly,

"I had to take it! Poor little dap got borned with five legs!" Thirza's shriek was almost as hysterical as Sal's had been.

"Lord have mercy on us, Lizzie! No wonder your poor Ma was in such a turmoil. Don't you know that's just wishing a freak or an imbecile mite to be born here within a twelvemonth. Fancy showing her an unnatural thing like that!"

Injecting sanity into the superstition-riddled situation, the nurse said that rabbits, malformed or otherwise, had nothing to do with human procreation.

Thirza shushed her, whispering.

"Lizzie may be sixteen, but she's as simple-minded as a six-year old and has shown no sign of being a woman grown.'

The nurse had first judged Lizzie to be about eleven, but her real age explained why her hair was still long while all the school age children of the family had cropped hair to eradicate the lice.

Lizzie's head would need inspecting. Really studying this thin, under-developed waif, another thought crossed the nurse's mind. She had witnessed the stick-thin, pot-bellied poverty among mining families during the lockouts, strikes, and unemployment of the nineteen twenties a few years earlier, but this seemed indefinably different. There was a curious roundness beneath the tattered dress and a haunted, almost animal fear was written on the child's undernourished face.

"Thirza, do you mind keeping the others occupied for a few minutes?" the nurse asked quietly. "I am going to ask Lizzie to slip off her dress."

The anxious inflexion of her voice made Thirza glance up questioningly and the message passing between the two women's eyes was instant and telepathic as Lizzie whimpered.

"No, not you! please."

"Come now child!" the nurse said briskly. Shivering with terror, abjectively submissive, Lizzie let the shapeless frock fall off her shoulders. Both women saw the bruising, the hand marks and the rounded stomach.

"Christ in heaven. Gentle Jesus, help us!" Thirza's voice was pure anguish as she tried to reject the obvious truth, but with Lizzie standing in just her knickers, there could be no doubt.

The nurse asked if Lizzie had a regular sweetheart, or was she one to fool around with the village lads. Thirza was certain that this was not so. In mind and body, Lizzie was a reticent, simple, almost infantile child, so timid she was incapable of getting herself a job.

Not then fully comprehending the true situation in this benighted and bullied household, the nurse said,

"Perhaps Lizzie's parents can tell me more?"

Lizzie's father had gone off following the threshing machine, his first employment for some time and it seemed to Thirza that Sal's anger was more devious than furious as she railed at her uncomprehending daughter.

"You've been out with them village boys, ain't you Lizzie? Now you admit it unless you want your father to take his strap to you! Do you want to get put away in some institution, locked up for years on end?"

Lizzie, bewildered and frightened, nodded, then shook her head.

"Say it then, say it was one of them boys that did it!"

Turning to the nurse, Sal stuttered.

"Lizzie's sixteen now, remember. I was married at her age and expecting too, not that that matters, except that she's over the age of consent."

Thirza suggested that the trouble might have been caused closer to home.

"You think what you like," Sal started sobbing, "but I've got twelve kids to feed, and when you try to prove what you're hinting, just remember that you might take the bread and butter out of their mouths. Bloody rabbit! I told you what would happen Lizzie, when you brought that thing in the house."

Thirza and the nurse agreed that Lizzie must be taken out of the danger right away, but the Poor Law Institution was the only solution available at the time. Sal made no objections, but the thought of poor inoffensive little Lizzie being incarcerated in the grim old prison-like building in the nearest city, was more than Thirza could bear.

"Lizzie," she said briskly, "your poor Ma has too many burdens and kids to contend with properly. I have none. How would you like to come and live with me for always. I do get a mite lonely at times."

Lizzie made no answer but went to collect her few personal

belongings, a broken string of glass beads and a torn piece of old blanket which she cuddled when she went to bed.

So Lizzie found a home in Thirza's lonely cottage, and there some four months later a premature, puny, brain-damaged child was born. No one could have lavished more love, care and attention than did Thirza, and in the few months that the baby survived, the young mother, still not fully comprehending her situation, cuddled her infant in the summer sunshine as if she was caressing a living doll.

The nurse had been a constant visitor from the day that she first discovered Lizzie's condition, collecting Thirza's weekly grocery order from the village, helping and keeping kindly watch over the ageing countrywoman with her simple-minded niece, and a baby with a life expectancy of nil.

It was easy to forget that hers was a temporary appointment to allow her nursing colleague to recuperate, and eventually the day came when she rode over to tell Thirza that she must soon leave.

She found Thirza washing nappies. Together they went to look for Lizzie who had carried her baby into the meadow beyond the back garden gate.

They found her on her knees amidst the tall sorrels and daisies, crooning tunelessly to the baby lying limp and lifeless in her arms. Thirza held her close as the nurse took the dead child from her, Lizzie looking perplexed by the tears on the nurse's cheeks.

"You said that five-legged rabbit was bad, didn't you Aunt Thirza? He made me take it! It's his fault ain't it?" She looked at Thirza for confirmation.

"Who Lizzie?" The nurse asked gently, hoping to clear up her suspicion of incest. All she got by way of answer was Lizzie whimpering. "I don't want to be hurt bad again, nor locked up!" The subject was dropped. It took all Thirza's courage to take Lizzie for her usual Friday shopping. The regulars were all there, excited and anxious to tell her that Lizzie's drunken father had been knocked down. He had staggered in front of the nurse's motorbike and had landed in Plough Lane ditch.

"No bones broken!" The shopkeeper assured her, "but while he was floundering in the mud half-drowned with panic, the nurse accidentally blacked his eye as she hauled him out. He's got some diabolic bruising, but that's only to be expected when you think of being prodded by that sharp upright metal front number plate.

'Fat lot of thanks she got for her trouble and bothering to look after him this morning. Pearce the postman reckoned he could hear him hollering half a mile distant when the nurse poured liniment over his bruised unmentionables to stop infection setting in. It seems that 'Slap-Cabbage Sal!' won't need to worry now about him breeding babies like some old buck rabbit, or being unlucky enough to have number thirteen for some time to come."

"Talking of rabbits!" Sadie Walls interjected. "Now the nurse is leaving I wondered if we ought to give her a little farewell present seeing how helpful she has been. I've got an old-fashioned brooch that was Grandma Walls. It's a lucky rabbit's foot mounted on silver. Do you think she'd like that, Thirza?"

Before Thirza could answer, Lizzie spoke out.

"Don't give her that or she might get a poor little baby same as I did."

"Lizzie, you do talk nonsense," Thirza interjected. "Come on girl, help me pack these groceries, we must get back now!"

Hand in hand with her ageing Aunt, the artless, immature girl walked back along the country lanes towards the only safe sanctuary of love that she had ever known.

Chains of Daisies

Cast ne'er a clout until May be out was a saying that most country people agreed with, although there were differing opinions about the exact time of year intended. The more venturesome believed it to be permissible to shed a few layers of winter clothing as soon as the blossom on the hawthorn bushes began to bloom. More cautious souls waited for the treacherous month of May to be safely finished before attempting to cast off their winter combinations or flannel petticoats.

Some of my classmates at the village school were literally stitched into flannel undershirts from Michaelmas until June, regardless of any minor heatwave that April or May might bring. My Mum was not averse to protecting my chest with a piece of flannel soaked in oil of wintergreen and goose grease, kept in place with long tapes, and tucked out of sight beneath an itchy woollen vest. My liberation from being muffled in cold weather clothing always came toward the end of May, on one special celebratory day of joyous freedom, a landmark in the year.

I loathed the brown, concertina-wrinkled stockings of winter, since they had to be held up by tight garters that did nothing for my circulation and frequently fell down around my ankles. Otherwise they were held aloft by home-made suspenders sewn to my liberty bodice. Any slight exertion was liable to send the buttons pinging so, whichever method of suspension my mother favoured to keep my long skinny legs encased for the winter, my stockings were always at half mast, leaving a gap between knee and knicker prone to every cold wind that blew.

The fleecy-lined knickers that I wore stretched with each trip to the washtub, extending upwards to my armpits and sagging into a voluminous elastic-gathered bunch around each leg. Vest, combinations and petticoats were topped by a thick skirt and jumper but, come Empire Day, all this was changed. With my winter-clothing chrysalis discarded, the summer 'me' emerged like a scrawny specimen of a Cabbage White butterfly, white cotton vested, knickered and petticoated.

Gone were the drooping winter stockings in favour of cotton socks, and the boots in which, like most country children, I plodded through the mud of winter, were put aside. On Empire Days I was allowed to wear white canvas shoes or sandals that, by comparison, were thistledown upon my feet.

Freedom from muffling winter-weight clothing was but one factor that made the ritual of our Empire Day celebrations seem so special, the one day in the year when I ran eagerly to school.

The year my father donated a flagstaff for School Field I was sure I would burst with pride. I watched while he felled the tallest pine tree on the woodland skyline. I rode beside it as Dad's horses hauled it home on a rumbling timber tug. Weathered, planed and painted, it was taken round to School Field, waiting to be dedicated and erected when that year's Empire Day ceremony began.

I left home early that morning, taking the short cut through a wood green with springtime, where a myriad huge black ants industriously scurried around their teeming mounds in regimented order, where wild anemone and heady-scented bluebells carpeted the woodland floor on each side of the path. As I hurried along past hawthorn hedges heavy with pinky-white blossoms smelling like vanilla junket, unsheared sheep and fat, panting lambs stared steadfastly as if they envied the fact that I had shed my winter fleece.

Under horse chestnut trees, with candle blossom all ablaze in celebration of summer, I ran on through Parsonage Path, flanked by hedges of white and purple lilac, philadelphus and laburnum in full flower, until I reached School Lane. In overcrowded cottage gardens, stocks and riotous-coloured wall flowers were kept in some semblance of order by the Guardsman-straight lines of yellow and red tulips lining either side of the front paths.

Other children had reached School Field before me, wandering in the still-wet grass with their white sandals turning damp-grey in the dew as they picked the longest-stalked daisies they could find. The object of the exercise was to make the longest, strongest daisy chain before the school bell went. Trooping triumphantly into the schoolroom with three or four lengths twined round our necks, the most despicable sabotage one could inflict on a fellow pupil was to nip off the daisy heads, so that the chain fell apart and dropped to the floor.

With our schoolmaster in charge of the proceedings, one would never dare to stoop down and attempt to retrieve it, although the possession of a daisy chain was an all-important factor in this special day.

While pupils stood shuffling, hands on heads, and more than a promise of the cane for anyone caught talking, the 'big boys' helped to carry the school piano out of doors. Marching forth in columns, ever mindful of the fate threatened by the school-master to those who did not mind their manners, we mustered in lines before a circular slab of concrete with a hole at its centre. An assembly of honoured guests sat on chairs brought over from the village hall. Part of the fascination of the occasion was to watch them visibly shrinking as the tips of their chair legs sank lower and lower into the turf. The school governors and managers, Dad among them, the parson, several fussy-hatted ladies and, of course, His Lordship himself: all shrank before us.

The little ceremony ran to a set pattern, starting with the schoolmaster's speech of appreciation of the honour being bestowed on the humble village children by His Lordship's pres-ence. Then His Lordship had his say. Because he too, stuck to a recognisable routine, as soon as his first question left his throat, we were ready with hands thrusting upward, hoping to be the fortunate pupil called upon to answer. Could we tell him why we were all wearing daisy chains this morning?

Of course we could, yet if his silver-topped cane pointed in one's direction, country shyness made the pupil stumble on his words, stuttering and mumbling, while all the rest shouted the answer clear. We knew that there were as many branches of the British Empire as there were petals on a daisy, because he used the same theme every year.

We knew too that each flowering shrub around the perimeter of School Field was planted to commemorate those men who left our village to defend our Glorious Empire in the 1914–18 war. To break their branches was to damage and disparage the names of those who fought for us. It was almost treasonable, and an insult to our illustrious King.

At this point six big boys from the top class struggled to lift and carry the new flagstaff forward to the concrete base. Assisted by Charlie Cartwright, Lordy's steward and my father, they heaved it upright, carrying it forward like a wavering caber, to the accompaniment of mild clapping and infantile cheering. It tilted, wobbled and swayed. The parson stood ready to give his blessing, but ducked as the flagstaff dipped and fell to the ground.

"Damnation!" said my father. "The blasted wood has swelled with last night's dew."

Old Charlie Cartwright suggested that all it needed was a bit of planing, and while one of the big boys was dispatched to fetch a rasp and plane from the school woodwork cupboard, ceremonial faltered. Uncertainly, our honoured guests sat wondering how to maintain the dignity of the occasion to background noises of carpentry and old Charlie Cartwright's comments.

"If this is a plane, I'll stew my grandmother's toe-nails! You could ride bare boned to London on it and not get saddle sore!"

"Better take another smidgin off 'un, Harry. Let's try her now. Up a bit. Back aways. Hold it. Watch out missus. That's more like it."

As the flagstaff came to a vertical position and stayed there, Charlie turned to His Lordship, smiling, and said, "There you are, Sir. Didn't take more than the shake of a nanny goat's tail to do 'un, and ole Harry's flag pole be settled in snug as a flea in a tinker's nightshirt."

Our Empire Day celebration carried on. The parson intoned a diffident blessing and the flag was hoisted to loud applause. We sang rousing patriotic songs, and the more literate among us recited hunks of Kipling. Another prayer from the parson, then the schoolmaster reiterated the rules for our Empire Day race.

Spaced out according to age and sex, the course was ten times round School Field for the older pupils and twice for the smaller tots. Since there was an Empire Shield and a shilling awaiting the winner, the race became a free for all with no holds barred. We all knew that once the race was over and the shield presented, His Lordship would call for three cheers for King George, three more for our Glorious Empire, then ask if we would like a half-day holiday from school.

It happened every year, but we would still express complete surprise and shout "Yes please, Sir!" We willingly gave three more cheers for our bounteous kindly Lordship, and when we had finished the boys bowed and the girls all curtseyed to our honoured guests. Still wearing our daisy chain garlands we were free to race off home.

My pride that Dad had donated the flagstaff made me determined to win the Empire Day race and carry the shield home. But fate conspired against me, using my own mother's thrift and ingenuity as its involuntary tool.

Back in the depths of winter, one of my older sisters had brought home a woman's magazine that sometimes sported free dressmaking patterns. This particular copy included instructions and tissue-paper patterns for *Madam's Dream Trousseau*, complete with knickers, chemise and petticoat.

Studying the magazine carefully, Mum said she could see no reason why the pattern could not be adapted to make summer undies for my sister Nora and me. The book gave several alternative materials as being suitable. Lovely names like *nainsook, cambric, dimity, nun's veiling* or *angel skin crepe-de-chine*, but my Mum had some cotton sheets that had only worn thin in places, and she saw no reason why the stronger parts could not be utilised. A snag arose when someone used a small bit of the pattern to test the heat of their hair waving irons, having decided that it was just a small square of tissue and of no account, but Mum went on sewing, undaunted.

These then were the underclothes I wore on that Empire Day when I was so determined I would win the shield. I had realised there was something not quite right with the shape of my knickers as I hurried to school that morning. By the time we were lined up for the start of our minor marathon, I knew something was sadly amiss. I crouched down with the rest of my peers. Hampered or not, I had to run.

The inevitable happened before I had even negotiated the first corner. With two cotton legs and a buttonless waist band flapping round my ankles, I took refuge amongst the shrubs, hoping that some 1914–18 hero had no objections to my shedding my breeches behind his memorial bush.

"Ah, yes!" said my mother when I returned wearing a pair of the schoolmaster's wife's chaff sack bloomers that she insisted I used to cover my shame on my journey home. "I'll bet that little bit of spare pattern was a gusset fitting in there somewhere, I'll mend them up and stick a patch in the middle, and they will do for you this year."

Now Dad's flagstaff has crumbled to dust along with any reason to celebrate a glorious empire, but little girls still make daisy chains out in School Field and the tall flowering trees that surrounded it blaze with blossom in May.

The Crosscut Saw

Standing selfconsciously beside his mother, Tom watched the village shopkeeper rummaging amongst crumpled, yellowing tissue paper in a couple of dusty cardboard boxes. Having established that the large sized black cloth cap was the only item of mourning headgear that he had in stock, the shopkeeper adopted a take-it-or-leave-it attitude. He handed the cap to Tom's mother, saying she could please herself as to whether or not Tom should try it on for size.

Tom, a gangling, thirteen year old, studied his scuffed boots for a few embarrassed moments, then reluctantly balanced the wide peaked 'cheese cutter' black cloth cap on the side of his head. A grimy mirror behind the counter reflected his blushing image between the peeling, tarnished gilt lettering that advertised Peerless Erasmic Soap. The cap seemed to give him added height and maturity, making him keen to wear it. From his one experience of a talking picture show, Tom knew that the American city of Chicago swarmed with gangsters carrying guns in violin cases and wearing caps identical to this. He tilted it lower over one eye, surveying the effect until his mother clipped him smartly round the ears to remind him why the cap needed to be bought.

As she readjusted it to a less flippant angle, engulfing Tom's right ear and obscuring his forward vision, she noticed the price tag dangling at the back. Any possessive aspirations Tom had nurtured evaporated as his mother snatched the cap from his head.

"Five shillings and elevenpence?" Her voice was shrill with incredulity. "If I let young Tom follow his poor Grandfather wearing that thing, I'd half expect the old chap to lift the lid and sit upright in his coffin berating me for indulging in such wicked extravagant waste. It's a lad's cap I am willing to pay for, not the tithe rates on your shop!"

As she slammed the offending cap down on the counter, a piled up platter of stale doughnuts quivered in anguish. The top few, slipping and sliding, started a small sad avalanche, spreading snail trails of damp sugar across the unswept shop floor.

Glad to avoid the unpleasant atmosphere above counter level, Tom busied himself dusting dried mud and fluff from the retrieved doughnuts, and piling them up again almost as good as new.

Watching the abortive transaction with avid interest, was Alfie Pearce's Mum who lived in an adjoining cottage. She made sympathetic clucking noises in the direction of Tom's mother and added fuel to the fires of female indignation by observing that the selfsame type of cap could be purchased from the stall of the town market place for one shilling and sixpence, or one shilling and elevenpence if there was real rubber in the peak. Her Alfie had a cap Tom could wear for the funeral and all Tom's mother would need to purchase was a twopenny black Dolly tub dye.

Alfie Pearce's donated cap completely engulfed Tom's head. He loathed it. Black dye failed to shrink it and stuffing the headband with folded newspaper only heightened the illusion that his neck was a stalk supporting a monstrous mushroom of gigantic size.

For two days in succession his mother had indulged in a frenzy of baking, then early on the morning of his grandfather's funeral Tom helped his father carefully load baskets of crockery and trays of food on a home-built four wheeled truck. As they hauled it towards his grandfather's cottage on the far side of the village, it was difficult for Tom to realise that behind the drawn curtains of the front parlour, stiff, cold and unmoving, was the gentle old man who had always found time to tell Tom tales about his own boyhood. The one person in the world in whom Tom could confide his troubles, hopes and fears.

Alfie Pearce had regaled Tom with some horrific stories about dead people, ghosts and hauntings, so he was extremely apprehensive when his father suggested that they say their last good-byes to Grandad before the other relatives arrived.

Unashamedly clutching his father's hand, Tom entered the airless gloomy parlour and wondered aloud about the nightlights standing in saucers of salt that surrounded the coffin trestles. There was little comfort in his father's explanation that it helped to keep evil spirits away.

It seemed totally incomprehensible to Tom that his grandfather would never open his eyes and joke with him again, for he looked so naturally asleep that Tom walked on tip-toe to avoid disturbing his dreams.

Several unknown aunts and uncles arrived, speaking softly at first as they made excuses for not visiting the old man more often, but their voices became more strident as they crowded into the tiny house.

Tom's father was determined that the tenancy of the cottage should be relinquished in a tidy state, so while his relatives were staking their claims to various items as they awaited the arrival of the village undertaker, he took a pair of garden shears out to trim the front privet hedge. He knew he would invoke conjugal wrath by pottering around the muddy garden in his new white shirt and best blue serge suit, but an intolerable atmosphere of tension was developing among his older brothers and sisters that made him want to be by himself.

Tom cast envious glances through a gap in the drawn curtains but did not dare to defy his mother's orders that he stay clean and tidy, seen but not heard. He seemed to be in everyone's way, an unwilling listener to long standing family arguments that were being aired. Relatives that had not been near the place for years catalogued all the help they had supposedly given Grandad in secret, knowing that none could refute their claims now the old man was dead. Elbows were nudged, quietly spoken words fell like small stones rippling muddy puddles of innuendo. Smiling lips that could not mask the glaring looks cast in Tom's direction, murmured cautious observations about little pigs standing around and staying quiet because they were using their big ears.

It was beyond his comprehension that they could be bickering while Grandad lay peacefully asleep in his oak coffin in the middle of the room. If only the old man would wake from his dreaming, Tom knew that the arguing would stop in an instant.

A sudden impulse made him want to shout and use all the swear words that he knew to make his elders stop it, but the resinous woody smell of the coffin combining with the stuffy atmosphere of the crowded room, made him feel as if he was choking. A sharp prickling sensation overwhelmed him, as if a bed of stinging nettles had suddenly sprung up behind his eyes. He ran through to the back scullery where his mother was setting out trays of borrowed cups and saucers, trying to express an unhappiness for which he had no words, but she was too preoccupied with her own problems to show any reaction beyond observing that she was well aware that while the rest of her in-laws were jostling with each other to divide the spoils between them, Tom's father was skulking in the garden letting them take first pickings of what by any sort of justice, should be his. She was upset, hot, and flustered, and irritated at Tom's interruption.

"Do get out from under my feet boy. Busy yourself by finding some nice dry kindling wood from the shed. The weather is so damp and dreary, everyone will be thankful to hear a kettle singing for the teapot when we get back from the church."

The windowless wooden garden shed seemed colder and darker, steeped in a listening silence, as if it might be waiting to hear Grandad's hand upon the door latch. This place had been Tom's childhood refuge from his well meaning but sharp tongued mother.

Here he had listened to the harvest of yarns and stories that Grandad had gathered during the sixty years he had worked at the timber yard. His youthful days spent as an under-dog in a saw pit, getting covered in sawdust as he pulled a huge ripsaw through the tree trunks, provided many oft repeated tales. Later, of course, Grandad became a 'top-dog', guiding the ripsaw from above, and when the whole process became mechanised Grandad was made foreman of the yard.

All his tools were hung on nails and pegs around the shed walls. The iron-runnered wooden sledge, which he had made for Tom's Christmas present one snowy winter, still stood in the corner. Tom could recall every moment of that moonlit, freezing cold, white winter night when both Grandad and his father took him over to Banky Meadows to try it out. All three of them had laughed together, skimmed down the slopes together, tumbled in the snow together. His mother, coming with a lantern to find them because it was long past bed-time, was sure it would do Grandad's arthritis no good at all.

Tom and his father often helped the old chap cut logs for his fire, with Grandad for ever teasing Tom about having muscles no bigger than sparrow's kneecaps, and saying he would need a lot more meat pudding inside him before he would be man enough to use Grandad's huge crosscut saw.

Filmy with cart grease, and resonant as a church bell, the eight foot long saw still hung behind the shed door. Touching the cold steel that had been the old man's pride and joy somehow gave Tom comfort. Lifting it from the hook, Tom recalled Grandad's judgement that a man who owned such a tool need never go cold or hungry, as long as there were trees to be felled.

"Tom. Where are you? Get that wood and hurry up about it. We are just leaving for the church, so do come on!"

Suddenly aware that his mother was calling, Tom tried to replace the saw, but it bowed and bent back and forth. His mother was becoming more angry, so Tom hurriedly lowered the crosscut and let it slip down behind some old planks of timber, putting his sledge in front of it to prevent anyone getting too near to the sharp blade.

Running into the cottage, he found everyone silent and sombre, watching the coffin lid being screwed into place. Only in that moment did the finality of death hit Tom's senses. His mother gave him a clean handkerchief, jammed Alfie Pearce's borrowed cap down over his forehead, and straightened the sagging crepe armband on his sleeve.

The village undertaker, leading the procession, had forgotten to remove his cycle clips, but it did not seem to matter. Tom clutched a bunch of flowers that had been thrust in his hand, and walked along behind the six men who carried Grandfather's casket shoulder high. His father was one of the bearers. Tom could have sworn that he was weeping, but for the fact that grown men never cry. As if the heavens wept for Grandad's passing, rain fell steadily, making the dye from Tom's borrowed cap trickle black streaks down his face to mingle with tears. He watched the burial service through a mist of sobbing misery, then trooped back to the cottage with all the other mourners, hurrying to get out of the wet.

Enlisted into the task of handing round hot tea and piled up food plates, he was amazed to see the assembled relatives eating as if they had not been fed for a fortnight, before they started systematically sorting through Grandad's possessions. Raised voices discussed everything they touched, and he watched two staid lady aunts stage a tug of war on the narrow stairs, pulling at each end of a feather bolster like two thrushes fighting over a worm.

Taking advantage of his mother's absence in the scullery, Grandad's tin box was turned upside down on the kitchen table. Tom watched the group crowding round, discarding the medals Grandad had earned for attending Sunday School regularly, scrabbling for the few golden sovereigns they found in a small wash-leather bag. In their mourning clothes, they gave him the same feeling of nauseous revulsion that he had felt when he once saw a flock of rooks swoop on the carcase of a still warm dead lamb.

Attempting to find refuge in the shed, he found his oldest uncle piling a barrow full of Grandad's tools.

'Nothing much left in here boy, except that old sledge and those rough bits of timber,' he said sheepishly. The shed door swung back and forth in the wind. During this time, Tom's father had said little and eaten nothing, slipping away to clear up the clippings from the hedge. The rest of the mourners departed, with their loaded barrows, pony traps, and hand carts. Tom helped his father sweep out one empty room after another, the echoing silence broken only by his mother's complaining voice

38

listing various household items that should by rights have been hers.

"Woman," Tom's father said sternly, "the whole darned lot would have scarcely raised ten pound in an auction. My family came here greedy, grabbing, making excuses for staying away from my old Dad when they could have carried their guilty consciences back with all the stuff they grabbed. We did our best, and the old chap knew it. We had his love and no one can take that away, so we'll hear no more about it. Today has been about as much as I can stand!"

For a brief moment the red, raw weal of his father's private grief and anguish was so painful to witness that Tom hurried out to add a couple of old door mats and a broken windsor chair to the borrowed crockery already loaded on the four wheeled cart. Looking back at the windows as they left the cottage, Tom heard the shed door swinging back and forth in the wind. As his father went back to help him secure it, both saw the old sledge and knew they could not leave it behind. Tom suddenly remembered that he had left the crosscut saw down behind the planks of timber, and was delighted to find it still there.

Carefully wrapping it round with the mats, they put it on the cart, and in the gathering gloom of twilight, trundled their load back home.

The moon rose and the rain abated early that evening. Restless and unhappy, Tom's father suggested that they take the crosscut saw out and try cutting up logs from the felled tree in the fruit plantation behind the house.

Muffled against the dampness of the evening, they hauled the handcart across the sodden grass by the light of a hurricane lamp that reflected the wet branches as gleaming tinsel all around. Standing each side of the tree trunk, they made little progress, and the saw seemed to jerk and jump as if it had a will of its own. Then Tom learned the art of knowing when to pull the saw toward him, never actually pushing, and within a few minutes found a steady rhythm that made his toes and fingers tingle with warmth, and set the saw singing as it sliced through the wood. Using a beadle mallet and wedges, Tom's father split the sawn lengths into logs for the kitchen fire. In helping to load them, Tom's borrowed cap fell off and was trampled in the mud.

"For God's sake let the blooming thing lie there," his father told him. "I don't reckon your Grandad would want to see you dripping black dye and running around like a kid advertising gravy powder. If what the parson say be true, the old chap will be resting peaceful, knowing that the pair of us are out here thinking of him, and you man enough to handle his old crosscut saw."

A sudden chill gust of wind set the lamp flame flickering, Tom remembered Alfie Pearce's assertion that the spirits of dead people stay earthbound for about a fortnight, as something dark and shadowy swept across the wet grass. But if one is considered man enough to take the handle of an eight foot crosscut saw, he should not frighten easily. Tom turned defiantly to face whatever was moving behind him. It was just the shadow of a swaying branch.

May-time

Still wallowing in the trough of an agricultural depression, few villagers could afford the luxury of benevolence. Nevertheless, everyone in our rural community regarded King George V and Queen Mary's Silver Jubilee as a once in a lifetime opportunity to outdo Lockley and the other neighbouring villages with the extent of our celebrations, thus establishing our natural superiority once and for all. Every inhabitant became involved in the frantic preparations.

With committees springing up like mushrooms in a wet autumn, old enmities and unsettled scores were set aside in the welter of patriotic fervour. Folk who had previously ignored the existence of their next door neighbours, now combined forces to decorate the front elevation of their properties with red, white and blue favours, their new found friendliness as tenuous as the pennants of paper thin cotton that fluttered on thin string.

By virtue of his being an ex bunting tosser in the Royal Navy, old Jim Puddington took on the task of ensuring that even the most remote and isolated cottage sported some sort of patriotic emblem to honour King George V and his Queen.

Scratching hens had spoiled the effect my mother had hoped for when she planted white candytuft and blue aubrietia around the clumps of peony flowers in our old farmhouse garden. It did nothing for her nervous system when, to prove that we were patriots, I scrambled up to place a flag on a stick high up in the massive copper beech tree that spread its mighty arms to shield our home from the worst of the easterly winds. It hung there until the gales of the following winter shredded it to ragged ribbons, with few to notice that it was upside down. Those who did accepted it as just another example of my being born awkward, having the unfortunate habit of tackling every straightforward task *widdershins* or the wrong way round.

Just thirteen, this failing had caused me more than a few low spirited moments of rejection amid all the rush and bustle of preparations for the big day. Enthusiastically as the rest, I had bound cane hoops with silver paper, adding dozens of painstakingly made, crepe paper, red, white and blue roses, ready for our spectacular display.

Soon after our first rehearsal had begun, the long suffering soul who had volunteered to attempt to transform thirty lumpkin country children into flower wielding elemental sprites ducked out of allowing me to remain among those performing.

Her reasons were specific. My unfortunate tendency to take off in the opposite direction to everyone else was totally disruptive. I was so gauche, so completely left handed, I caused instant confusion to all around me. It was her expressed opinion that inside my drooping socks I blundered along on two left feet.

Appreciating my disappointment, she explained that at 5ft 9in, my height alone could ruin the sensational effect of her highly original finale, wherein the flower festooned hoops became one massive floral tribute of loyalty. Behind this the performers lined up, holding and completely hidden by a sheeting banner bearing the legend, *Long Live His Lordship And Her Ladyship. God Save Our King and Queen.*

It was vital that this production should go well, for we had competition. Because His Lordship's son and heir was once a day scholar at an august, exclusive and ludicrously expensive college for the sons of gentry, situated in the next parish, a group of the illustrious young gentlemen were going to honour our celebrations by presenting excerpts from a comedy. This was to be their contribution to the happiness of the day. This I knew, for on the previous evening an impromptu parish meeting had convened around my Mum's kitchen table.

In retrospect it seemed that the main items on the agenda were to munch away at still warm bread and cheese and sample Dad's home made beer. At the same time everyone was trying to co-ordinate the many and varied activities into some sort of order so that a Jubilee programme could be formed.

The parson's sister, being the only lady committee member present, looked askance at such rough fare, but declined Mum's offer of a seed cake and a cup of tea. She would not say no to a sip of fruit cordial, if Mum had any to offer. Mum gave her a full tumbler of cherry ale to keep her quiet.

From the fireside stool where I sat, supposedly reading, I watched her face assume the same colour as the contents of her glass. Slurring slightly, Parson's sister put forward the proposal that, since various farmers were contributing barrels of cider and beer for the men of the parish to drink the loyal toast to Their Majesties, Mum could provide a few bottles of home made fruit cordials to enable the distaff side of the village to pledge their loyalty too.

The motion was carried unanimously. Old Charlie Cartwright sitting near me, stage whispered to my Dad that he "bet the old gal would make sure she was put in charge of the bottles and come with a corkscrew in her hand."

Old Charlie confirmed that His Lordship had personally tele-phoned him about "Them college lads giving a bit of a comedy performance." He had jotted it down somewhere, but could not put a hand to the note just at that moment. He knew it was by one of their masters who taught Greek, or some other high flown lingo. A Mr. Risto-Fanies or some such double barrelled name. No matter what, the committee could thank him for a good laugh after the sketch.

The timing of the two entertainments hinged on the arrival of His Lordship and his party. With Her Ladyship, he was to attend the Service of Thanksgiving in Westminster Abbey, and at the conclusion hurry back to our celebration. He would then graciously give us a first hand account of this auspicious occasion, and present every child in the parish with a Jubilee medal and a mug. The village children would then present their patriotic spectacular, followed by the college's comedy play. Until our noble patron arrived, the main item in the day long festivities was a cricket match, the ladies of the village versus the men.

The rules of the match allowed one innings only, men to bowl underarm, batting with a hedge stake, women to bat or bowl by any method they chose.

Originally, twelve slightly daring or downright defiant souls had volunteered for the ladies team, but two dropped out. One was keeping a low profile, having got herself married with what was then regarded as shameful swiftness, while the other non starter admitted that she had the choice of respecting her husband's disapproving viewpoint or being thumped. All this I heard, ear-wigging at the meeting in our kitchen. Listening to my elders discussing the advisability of asking the parson to supplement the ladies team, since he was nought but an old woman, I longed to volunteer to fill the vacancy. With three older brothers, I learned early how to hit a ball and run. Rejection from the dancing display gave me the chance.

Most housewives produced their best cookery in readiness for the early hours of Jubilee morning, when Dave's milk float and our covered cart did the rounds of the parish, collecting all edible contributions to take them to the various tents and the huge marquee erected in Glebe Meadow. Jim Puddington's flags and bunting fluttered like lines of coloured washing as the black-smith's wife stacked row on row of Jubilee mugs on a sheet covered table by the tent flap entrance. There was an excited, chaotic kind of rush and bustle all around.

Alighting from three parked cars, a troop of white clad college lads, wearing effeminate looked pleated tunics, followed their dismal looking master. Presuming him to be the Mr. Risto-Fanies that had been noted down for Charlie Cartwright's attention, Charlie greeted him by name. The perplexed, pale face crumbled into a semblance of a smile, like creased tissue paper.

"How droll. Risto-Fanies indeed. Your ready wit will no doubt savour our excerpt from The Archarnians by the Athenian classical genius Aristophanes.'

Old Charlie nodded uncertainly.

Out on the field, the toss of a new Jubilee penny decided that the ladies cricket team were batting first. I was opening bat. Stifling my stage fright I walked out toward the wicket, watching the warm southerly breeze flutter the canvas of the marquee.

The ladies team had met with many cross currents of opposition and disapproval, caused by strait laced individuals who believed that any female flaunting herself by cavorting around Glebe Meadow with eleven leery and agile men must degrade and disgrace all womanhood.

The relevant Jubilee committee tactfully asked lady cricketers to "act with decorum and play soberly and suitably dressed." In no way could our ladies team captain have been accused of flaunting or attempting to arouse baser male passions. Inappropriately named Violet, she was totally lacking in feminine attributes. Heftily built, hearty voiced and clad in the washed-out looking shirts and breeches that seemed to be the entire content of her wardrobe, any stranger might well have believed her to be one of the more lusty members of the opposing team.

Her interpretation of the committee's advice on dress was to keep any part of the anatomy inclined to flop or wobble crepe bandaged or tightly corseted. Glimpses of bare flesh between suspendered stockingtops and bloomer elastic were taboo, and the fashionable, lace trimmed, wide-legged french knickers were definitely out.

Our team were conservatively clad for the occasion. Most wore hats, either straw or floppy, wide-brimmed floral cotton, while some favoured head bands or hair nets. With tall spiky dead grass in the outfield few risked wearing their best silk stockings. Instead they displayed thick cotton lisles and flat heeled shoes. Even the more sprightly chose calf length skirts and severe blouses or subdued summer frocks.

Conforming to the prevailing proprieties, some wore white cotton gloves. In what had seemed at the time to be an inspirational moment, I had borrowed the outfit my older, fashion conscious sister had made for her Saturday afternoon tennis sessions. It was a blue, linen garment, with a bloused bodice and knee-length divided skirt. Skinnier than the garment's owner, I pulled in the waist with a wide, red, patent leather belt. In conjunction with my white socks, white gym shoes and the red bow that was supposed to hold back my long hair, I thought I had struck the right Jubilee effect.

Others whittled away my self confidence. Parson's sister, who held herself to be above such low class frivolity, said that for an almost grown girl I was dressed flightily, and exhibiting far too much bare leg. Granny Gammon asked what sort of contraption I was supposed to be wearing. With that red belt around my middle I looked like six pennyworth of long stalked rhubarb tied together with string. There was no time to run home and change.

The scorekeepers, male of course, chose the side of the refreshment tent as the best place to chart the match as it progressed. From the line of empty tankards set before them, they already viewed the state of the pitch through the amber glow of farmhouse brewed cider and ale. Albert Parsley, still spry then, was our opponent's choice of umpire. They grouped around him, listening as he ran through the rules of the game. Our chosen umpire, Big Bertha Pye, allayed any fears that our opponents might try doubtful tactics. This truly liberated and muscular lady advised my batting partner and I to imagine that we were "clumping them fools around the yud with a copper stick." She promised that any of them inclined to argufying would feel the back of her hand around their ears.

Nervously aware of a small, sporadic burst of clapping, I took guard with my bat. Old and unoiled, it had lain in the toolshed since the days when my brothers and sisters could have formed a cricket team of their own. Now the bat's infrequent use was for driving hazel spars into the straw of loosened thatch.

Bowling the first ball of the game, Slippy Springer sent down a spinning snorter. With a muck shovelling kind of stroke I helped it on its way.

"Run," I yelled, scuttling up the pitch towards my batting partner. She paused in her attempt to straighten the brim of her hat, looked vaguely surprised to see me, and in answer to my loudly repeated entreaty said, "Run Jo? Do you mean me? Which way?"

I tore back to the safety of the crease, while Bertha explained the finer points of run scoring, but this made the poor soul more confused. She set off to meet me before Slippy bowled the second ball. There were loud appeals. "Howzat?"

Still out there batting, with six wickets down in as many

overs and only fourteen runs on the scoreboard. I was joined by the doughty Violet. The grinning fielders who had gathered like flies around a jam jar, moved well back from the wickets. Two or three of her swiping agricultural strokes followed in every successive over, with myself scoring an occasional single, but mostly tearing up and down to keep my end up. When the limited overs of our innings ended we had scored fifty seven runs.

There was a slight altercation before the men started their innings, due to Big Bertha's refusal to accept the sawn-off posts they intended to use for batting. She would only settle for hedge stakes, literally taken from the hedge. That the young bullocks in the adjoining pasture took advantage of the gap in the hedge seemed to her to help make for more jollifications. Heaven knew there were enough idle folk standing around to drive them back. Time and again the makeshift bats broke and splintered.

The men's run rate rose, but wickets fell, thanks to some highly doubtful umpiring decisions. They needed three more runs in four more overs when Lordy's limousine was sighted turning in along Church Lane. Adhering strictly, and in our case thankfully, to the prearranged plan, stumps were drawn and our game came to an end.

Having attended the Royal Service of Thanksgiving in London, His Lordship was too tired to make long speeches. A rearrangment of the programme gave him the opportunity to watch the children's patriotic spectacular before he presented the medals and mugs.

Grass stained and windswept I watched the display from the back of the tent, then had to push my way through the assembled adults to collect a Jubilee medal and mug from the hands of Her Ladyship. She scowled at my untidy appearance. The handle of the mug she held towards me was, and still is, cracked.

The young college scholars then presented their Greek Comedy, but this left everyone slightly baffled, since it entailed two dozen pimply boys chanting and speaking a strange language. Everyone clapped politely, taking their cue from Lordy and the parson, who, in his speech of thanks, pronounced it "most enlightening, witty and extremely droll."

At the freely given village tea party Grace was said and this was followed by the first of many loyal toasts. For children this meant powdery lemonade, but for their elders the choice was tea, farm brewed ale or cider, or home made wine. Granny Gammon had put down a special five gallon crock of wine the previous summer, and among all the other prized and coveted recipes there was nothing to touch her wild strawberry wine. It matched the flame of the beacon fire of that happy evening, a magical ingredient of a celebration long remembered and long past.

Rats Castle

Perhaps our more affluent forbears believed it to be wrong that those requiring their charity should enjoy receiving it. There seems to be no other explanation for building Butchers Row, a terrace of four alms cottages a mile out from the village at the end of a woodside track. The Butchers Bequest, was a phrase that those who had their roots in the village often heard, but rarely understood. We only knew that someone in the 18th century, a Butcher by name or trade, had bequeathed the money to build and maintain the four houses.

Generations of trustees must have taxed their brains, fairly allocating the cottages at either end to *men abiding in lawful wedlock, who by bad favour or an act of God have no habitation for themselves Their Kin or Kine.* Beneficiaries for the two centre cottages were only eligible providing that they were *righteous, sober-minded bachelors, in no way blasphemous, clean in manner*

49

and of good repute, or *industrious spinsters of honest birth and proven virtue.* How this was to be proved was not defined.

By the time my generation came along the fabric of the cottages and the trust fund were both in an advanced state of decay and their official name of Butchers Row was seldom used.

We called them Rats Castle and anyone who lived there did so as a last resort. Grubby Jack, who lived in one of the centre cottages, must have had his application for tenancy granted by trustees in a very liberal frame of mind. Far from being sober, clean and in no way blasphemous, Jack was frequently as tight as a tick, rejected soap and water since it washed one's natteral iles away, and had a vocabulary of oaths and swear words colourful enough to curl the devil's horns.

Maybe his unsociable habits encouraged the trustees to bend the rules in his favour, since this would remove him from the close vicinity of the village. If his uncouthness caused his neighbours at Rats Castle inconvenience, beggars could not be choosers, and they were in no situation to complain. Next to Jack lived Miss Minnie Wood, a timid woman of uncertain age, struggling to exist in a state of half starved gentility. If there were but dry bread to offer, Miss Minnie would slice it thinly, place it on one of *dear Mama's* china plates and serve it on a tray complete with starched white cloth.

Her history was one of devotedly nursing a bedridden, domineering, dear Mama, until ultimately Miss Minnie was left to face the fact that when Mama expired Mama's Army widow's pension expired too, leaving her daughter penniless, untrained, and without a soul in the world to care about her plight. The cottage at Rats Castle was her only refuge, and somehow she existed as church organist and part time librarian, stamping our library tickets every Tuesday afternoon.

She made beautifully patterned pillow lace, which she sent off to the city once or twice a month, but so quiet and unassuming was she that to most of the parishioners little Miss Wood was affectionately known as Minnie Mouse.

When old Zekey Dodds fell from the top of a corn rick the chances were that he would never walk again. The farmer who employed him needed his tied cottage for his replacement, so of necessity Zekey and his wife Hester moved into the end cottage at Butchers Row. Slowly Zekey became more mobile and with

Hester's help transformed the large end plot into a productive cottage garden.

This demanded constant vigilance against marauding rabbits, pheasants and pigeons that raided his vegetables from the safety of the nearby wood. The contest was not one sided. Many a pheasant was tempted by the currants Zekey placed under a tilted bushel basket, balanced by a stick of kindling wood. His skill with a catapult thinned out the rabbit population and provided many a main course for themselves and Minnie Mouse.

A farm worker's tied cottage could be either a blessing or a curse. The minimal rent, if rent was paid at all, cushioned the lowness of his wage, but there was the ever present threat of dismissal. That could mean instant eviction should the employer's displeasure be invoked. From the farmer's point of view, a good reliable farmhand was someone to be shown every consideration, and a free cottage near to hand was essential if they were to settle down and be content.

In the last years that it was inhabited the remaining cottage at Rats Castle constantly supplied the need for temporary accommodation for homeless farmhands searching for new jobs, and seemed to change occupants as frequently as most country people changed their winter sheets.

Hester Dodds and Minnie made the best of their surroundings, and had Jack not lived between them, with his filthy windows curtained by old sacks, the cottages would have been the picture of rustic charm. Minnie's one up two down home was packed full of dear Mama's heavy furniture, with scarce a space between the pictures on the walls. The doorstep was hearth stoned, the door knob polished, and the rambling Dorothy Perkins roses disguised the fact that damp beneath the flaking limewash was eroding the wattle and daub walls.

Apart from seeing Miss Minnie scuttling back and forth on her village duties, no one gave much thought to Rats Castle until a new cowman came to Oak Farm. Although his family increased the school roll by eight, besides those that his wife pushed around in a tattered pram, he seemed determined to get the sack from the day he started. Inevitably he did, and straight away demanded to be housed by the Butcher's Bequest. He moved into the first cottage of the row, his kin and kine being twelve children, two goats, a dog and a scattering of fowl.

He bullied Miss Minnie and Hester, knowing that Zekey being crippled, was unable to retaliate. The goats played havoc with their garden crops and were liable to butt them as they pegged out their washing.

There were frequent swearing matches with Jack, who for once came second best. The day that he went to his little house at the end of the garden path and found it occupied by a nanny goat and two hens Jack decided that he must act. The vicarage study was foreign ground to Jack, but as chairman of the Butcher's trustees the vicar was the man he went to see.

"That poor dear lady next to me daren't step out of her door between choir practice and early communion. There's been such a hammering and yammering going on that the pictures have fallen off the walls," he complained.

The vicar suggested he should go and try sweet reason, but Jack took a poor view of that. As his next line of attack he held consultation with the group of men who usually foregathered on the forge wall on Saturday afternoons. That night, soon after dark, several people carrying tins, rook scarers, rattles and iron frying pans, made their way along the track to Rats Castle. Gathering silently in front of the first cottage they began to beat, bang or rattle a steady cacophony of contempt.

By the time Miss Minnie came home from matins the next morning her neighbours had gone. Jack and Zekey looked inside the swinging open door.

Every piece of burnable wood had been torn or sawn out. Staircase, bedroom floors, roof rafters and even the purlins of the house.

"Strewth," said Jack, "the whole damned lot is liable to fall down."

One by one the tenants of Rats Castle were found new accommodation and it stood empty, dropping into roofless decay. Inaccessible, but visible from the grand new trunk road, Rats Castle ruins still remains as four broken chimney breasts that in spring provide nesting places for jackdaws and in summer are clothed with wild clematis and an old pink rambling rose.

The Trees of Time

During the 1880's young Robert Packman persuaded his employer to let him convert a large acreage of old pasture land on the estate into fruit orchards. Neighbouring farmers were unanimous in their belief that to have appointed young Robert as a farm bailiff was a rash decision and encouraging his hare brained radical notions was the fastest route to a failed farm and the bankruptcy court.

The farmers who worked alongside their men through summer drought and the mud of winter knew the land too well to indulge in daft experiments. Grassland fed sheep and cattle, and arable soil could make a profit from potato crops and grain. Only a city bred landowner with more wealth than agricultural wisdom would indulge an inexperienced bailiff's whim, and wait around watching his pastures being ruined for the sake of fruit trees that might or might not grow.

Unperturbed, young Robert set six horse teams to pull the heavy ploughs tearing up rough grassland and cultivating until the tilth of the soil was fine enough to trickle like sand through Robert's hands. Then he planted his trees.

They were sapling thin, bending wherever the whim of the wind took them until Robert drove in sturdy stakes to support them, binding live and dead wood together with straw ropes. The rabbits gnawed through the bark of the young trees, killing them by the dozen, but Robert replanted, protecting each scion with a wire netting shield. Under sown with fine grass and white Dutch clover, the orchards grew lush with the greenness of early summer. Mown with scythes they yielded fodder and when the sheep flocks were brought into shelter for the winter it was the new orchard that they grazed.

If Robert's employer was only a part time farmer, having more interest in the city than in his country estate, his son was different. Cared for by nursemaids, taught by a tutor and kept far from the social whirl of his parents' high society town life, the young boy spent his formative years in the country, having more contact with Robert Packman and the estate staff than with his own parents. Only on rare or great occasions did he reluctantly enter the other circles his parents moved in. Then he would thankfully return to the country and report what he had seen.

Soon after Robert's orchards were established the boy accompanied his parents to London for Queen Victoria's Diamond Jubilee. One of the Royal Princes had asked for his impression of the royal procession and the marching of the soldiers. The Young Master replied that "they were all in straight rows, whichever way one looked at them. Just like Robert's cherry trees." The Royal Prince, indulging a young boy's interest on a day when the pomp and ceremony of Empire was at its peak, commanded that when the young master became a fruit growing farmer the pick of his first crops should be sent to grace the table of the royal household. This too was excitedly reported to Robert.

"By God, boy. Then we'll grow fruit that is fit for a king."

By the time the trees were really starting to bear fruit the boy had become a young man, foregoing his rural interests to follow the family tradition of serving in the Army, much against his will. He came home on leave late one evening when the trees were all in full blossom to find the orchards under a pall of smoke haze from innumerable bonfires lit beneath the trees. With frost in the air Robert was taking no chances.

Equally determined that there would be fruit fit to offer the royal household that year, the young man stayed in the orchards, helping Robert stoke the fires all that night. Both Robert and he looked like smoke blackened scarecrows by daylight the next morning. Ice film coated the yard pond, but in the orchards not one spray of cherry blossom had been singed by the tell tale brown of frost.

The Young Master gave instructions that Robert send him a wire when the Black Heart and Napoleon cherries were ready. But the year was 1914 and along with the rest of his regiment he was mobilised for war. By the next fruit-picking season he had become a name on the casualty lists, posted as "Missing."

Robert went on tending his orchards, determined that if his employer's son should ever return there would still be fruit fit to offer a king.

When the autumn leaves from the cherry trees formed a red carpet, word came that the young man had been found. Shell shocked and with one leg amputated he was in a Belgian hospital, neither comprehending nor caring whether he was alive or dead.

Surrounded by attendants and nurses, he was brought back to the country to recuperate. This failed to bring the slightest improvement to his blank indifference. His scarred mind was imprisoned behind a high encircling wall. Robert's employer instructed him to report to the sick room each day to talk about the orchards in the hope that this might rekindle some of the interest in fruit growing that the young man had previously shown. It was a useless exercise achieving nothing but blank stares. Back stairs gossip among the servants spoke of him being moved to a hospital for brain damaged heroes, but Robert Packman was convinced there must be a way to set him free.

A silent bedroom with servants standing around like paid mutes at a funeral seemed a highly ineffective method. Asking no one's permission Robert carried the invalid downstairs then took him out to the orchards, wheeling him in a basketwork bath chair. As soon as he had made sure that the young man was safely settled, Robert resumed his tree pruning, talking as he worked.

"Your father can fire me just as easily as he hired me," he called down. "But I've brought you here out of everyone else's way to tell you privately that you make me puking sick. These ruddy trees have more sense than you, for all that you are supposed to be an educated gentleman. When a gale comes tearing in amongst them, they bend with it, letting it sweep past them. They don't curl up their roots and wither because the roar of the wind has been too loud for them to stand. Trees understand that a lost limb or a broken branch doesn't mean they are finished. It makes them more determined to sprout fresh wood, put down deeper roots and grow. When the storms and gales have passed they stand up straight like rows of soldiers, lifting their arms to the sky.

"Once you were keen to keep a promise and offer fruit from here fit for a king. You were the pick of the crop old son. You were the best we could offer. Your bark took a bit of a tanning and you lost a branch on the way. Now you can either stay in that bloody chair like a log of rotten wood, with the wood lice of self pity gnawing you into a heap of nothing or get off your backside, shore up what is left of your lopped limb, then let the rest of your branches reach up for the sun to make them grow straight again."

From beneath the trees Robert heard a harrowing howl, like a trapped vixen baying. Rushing down the ladder he saw the young man sitting with his arms raised upwards, all his soul's agony imprinted on his uplifted face. The torment and anguish were expurgated in one screamed phrase, "Oh Christ. Help me Robert."

Robert held him close like a father comforting a frightened child, till his tears were done.

The orchards flourished and so did the Young Master. Fruit from the estate graced many a royal banquet and Robert's authoritative advice became sought after and well known. As his trees grew taller he became more bent and round shouldered, until one day he decided that he and the orchards he had planted were long past their prime. It was time they were both rooted out to make way for new growth.

"An orchard needs a life-time of tending," he told his

employer. "You must find some young keen man to tend the replanting."

Knowing that his own days were numbered, old Robert Packman deliberately took up his axe and started to cut the old trees down.

The Ranks of the Elite

Hidden by the thick hawthorn hedge that used to grow along the twisting steep gradient of Folly Hill was a small secluded hollow, shaped as if some giant hand had scooped it from the steep grassy bank. When sheer accident caused me to discover its existence I was unappreciative of the wild violets and primroses that grew there. I was flat on my face, vaguely conscious of a fern frond probing one nostril, and a wet tongued collie dog licking my face. My forward vision was totally obscured by a pair of farm boots and corduroy trouser legs tied just below the knees.

"What in tarnation be you a-doing here Jo? You fair put the wind up me, for I thought I'd found a dead 'un! I only came up here because old Patch was yapping about as if he had found an old ewe on her back, and here you be looking as if you have been pole axed."

I recognised Shup Woolley's voice long before his face would stay in focus. As he helped me to sit up he continued, "My stars! You look fair mazed and muzzy! How did you get here?"

I had no idea what had happened, yet irrationally I was glad that it was the old shepherd who had found me, and not one of my tut tutting aunts.

They were always imploring me to behave in a more lady like manner, and my Aunt Flo had predicted that when I stood before the pearly gates of paradise on the day of Judgement I would hitch up my skirts and try to climb them. She had no doubts that I would find them closed! At fifteen, I showed no sign of becoming elegant, or refined, which seemed to worry my older and more distant relatives a good deal.

Patch, the collie, continued to lick my face with his long wet tongue, while I tried to marshal my confused thoughts in a brain that had suddenly become as retentive as a wide meshed sieve. I was convinced that my plight was somehow connected with being lady like, yet Shup said that I had been rambling on about the day that Harry Applethorn, our old waggoner, tried to teach me to ride a horse.

As I explained to Shup, that incident occurred long before my fifth birthday, when Harry lifted me onto the bare back of a placid old shire mare. All four of the mare's legs seemed to be moving in different directions to its bony spine, so I bawled and hollered that I was slipping and would be trampled underfoot. Harry was equally adamant that I stayed where I was.

"You've got elbows and knees, ain't you?" Old Harry said sharply. "Just you use them to stay on and ride, young 'un. This world is divided between Haves and Have nots. The Haves ride, while the rest plod through life on their own flat feet. Stay put unless you want to be a Have not and never walk when you can ride."

Taking Harry's advice, I spent much of my childhood cadging lifts on farm carts, timber tugs, milk floats, even dust carts, or the rear carrier of my brother Stan's old bike. Even so, it was unlikely that I would be riding a horse through one of Shup's lambing pastures. As Shup said, there were no hoof prints on the turf. My breathing was making odd wheezy noises reminiscent of the chapel harmonium on Sunday nights. A baby rabbit, defying Patch and scudding to a burrow under the hedge, seemed to be a jumbled part of my present state, but that made no sense at all. With does in kindle and bucks too rank tasting to eat in springtime, this was the close season for rabbiting, so there was no way that I could have been out in the steep banked pasture poaching other people's rabbits by setting hingles or wire snares.

I drew no formal wages for helping my parents with the farm so rabbit catching provided a source of income, making my finances at their lowest ebb each spring. My addled brain registered the fact that I had needed cash for some urgent reason, but all Shup's attentive prompting could not make me remember why. Sufficient for that moment that I attempt to get vertical instead of horizontal. All the time Harry Applethorn's remarks about being a lady and riding kept repeating like a cracked gramophone record in my mind.

As I sat up, an oast house across the valley seemed to sway from side to side, like the pendulum of Elsie Dalton's grandfather clock. Mrs. Dalton was somehow part of the confusion. She was real enough, so I concentrated all my thoughts on her.

She was so houseproud that Shup was sure that she dusted and polished her husband, Wally, each night before she would allow him to go to bed. Her zeal extended beyond household possessions. Wally's must have been the only chicken farm where the hen houses had their windows polished every week. Wally owned an old motor bike and side car, and no royal coach could have had more wax polish lavished on it. Elsie covered it with a dust sheet in the shed when it was not in use.

My Dad used to sell the Daltons the tail corn for chicken food and every time I called there, I cast envious glances at the ladies bicycle that was suspended by two hooks on their corn store wall. It was wrong to covet other folks property, but I could have found so much use for the bike that Elsie, as a prim and proper young matron, felt too dignified to ride. When I approached Wally about the chances of her selling it he promised that I would have first refusal if she did.

Inordinately proud of his fastidious wife, Wally was very conscious of the fact that he had taken her away from her city world of service in genteel households, where piped water was taken for granted. Just as I would have given much to own Elsie's bike, so did Wally wish he could offer her some of the modern facilities she had sacrificed to become a chicken farmer's wife.

With the prospect of a happy event impending, Wally informed me that Elsie was now willing to sell her bicycle, but this came when my prospect of buying it seemed almost nil.

Aunt Flo would have looked upon it as a case of the devil helping the wicked, but a series of happy coincidences gave me a chance. The selling price was thirty shillings, fifteen of which my more affluent older sister lent as a long term loan. The opportunity to raise the rest presented itself when my Dad bought a sundry collection of drinking troughs at a farm sale. Among them was a huge cast iron bath tub, the sort of which Elsie Dalton still dreamed. Saltpetre worked wonders on restoring the enamel, and green oxide paint gave the exterior a new lease of life. Having hammered wooden barrel spigots into the bung hole and overflow opening, I took the bath tub round to the delighted Daltons on a cart.

Thus did I become the proud owner of a high framed bicycle with a wicker basket on the handle bars. Instructing me on how to ride and keep my balance, Wally suggested it would come easier if I headed downhill. Folly Hill was one of the steepest in the district, so in my ignorance it seemed the best place to try.

Sitting beside Shup and Patch, my clearing brain recalled the thrill of travelling downhill ever faster toward the bend of the road, then the breathless panic of being airborne as I sailed clean over the hedge. Still shaky on my feet and with a dull thudding headache I followed Shup as he cut a passage through the thorny hedge. My newly acquired bike lay bent and buckled and as Patch lifted his leg against it Shup reckoned the old dog was simply expressing an opinion on its sorry state.

"This old heap of junk will need more than a touch of the blacksmith's magic hammer and you need to have your head looked at, so I'll see you safely home. You and me are Have-nots like old Harry said, and by the looks of this scrap iron it will be a long time before you join the ranks of the elite and ride."

Kubla Khan

Perhaps the supper time discussion about the amount of work involved in preparing our Christmas poultry orders invoked the nightmare. I dreamed I was plucking feathers from penguins on an ice floe, and woke up shivering with the cold.

Too drowsy to differentiate between fact and fantasy, I wondered why my bare feet were still on a frozen surface when the rest of me was snuggled under the blankets of my bed. Lighting the bedside candle meant moving my feet from the metal bed-warmer that spent each winter day in the kitchen range oven and each night in the nether regions of my bed. Never before had it gone cold before morning, but my bedroom felt as cosy as an ice box. Had I been spartan enough to consider a cold water wash in the basin on the marble topped washstand, it would have been impossible, for the jug was filled with solid ice. I dressed quickly, piling on layers of warm clothing, but nothing seemed to stop the cold that seeped into my bones.

To be the first one up in the morning was an unusual experience. The eerie silence enveloping the old house was accentuated by the plodding pendulum of the clock on the kitchen mantel-shelf counting time.

Relying on the open fire of the old wood burning stove for heating, cooking, and boiling water, we always made sure that there was a good supply of dry kindling sticks left in the kitchen overnight. The dry twigs flaring under the kettle soon provided boiling water to wash with, and to brew tea in the brown earthenware pot. By the time Mum and Dad came downstairs, I was warming my hands round a half pint mug of hot tea.

Our early routine never varied, no one sitting down to breakfast until all the farm animals had been watered and fed. Dad's first task was to see to the horses in the stable, while I fed and milked Dolly, the shorthorn cow. We then combined forces to mix pig meal, cut chaff, and carry fodder to the young bullocks fattening in the stockyard, opening up the chicken-houses to feed Mum's free ranging hens on our way back to the kitchen and our morning meal.

Pleased with my early start that morning, I put on a thick old coat, and pulled my boots on. Despite their overnight drying by the hearth, and the coat of greasy dubbin, they still struck damp and stiff to my chilblained feet. My storm lantern was a feeble glow-worm wavering along the passageway. The massive bolt and latch on the back door was frozen fast.

Dad helped me heave and tug to force it open, spilling a heap of snow on the doormat, seeping in the top of my boots. A coal shovel from Mum's brass companion set and a tin lid tacked on a broom handle were inadequate tools to tackle the five foot drift blocking the doorway, then dig a path to get garden spades and shovels from the shed. After an hour of hard work we were still floundering around trying to get to the farm buildings where the animals were loudly demanding to be fed. My stomach rumbled persistently, thinking of our warm breakfast spoiling in the oven while we wondered how to water the stock.

The yard pump was covered in icicles, like grease from a snuffed candle. The rope around the well's winding roller was glazed with thick ice, a coiled snake in aspic jelly, and with the winding handle set fast, as if in concrete, there was no means of getting water. The horses began chuntering for their drinking buckets, the bullocks lowed beside their frozen trough, porkers squealed insistently, and the old boar, Genghis Khan, heaved his great bulk up to rest his front trotters on the top rail of his sty. His ultimatum was as plain as if he had spoken. His bucket of pig meal would be delivered immediately, or he would break down his fence.

Even in his more contented moments, Genghis had the savage look of an overweight mongolian warrior with six inches of impacted snow raising the level of his sty floor, he needed little aggravation to bring him blundering over the top. We knew that a bad tempered boar could be the most dangerous of all farm animals, and did not relish the prospect of rounding him up in the snow and ice.

We could think of only one way to get water quickly, and this meant taking a sledgehammer and an iron spike to break a hole in the ice on the pond. This involved walking out on the slippery jetty to squat like a pair of Laplanders hammering and hacking to make a hole in the ice. With only a flimsy frozen hand-rail to hold while one scooped up water in an iron bucket, walking that glassy plank was a downright dangerous operation and by the time we had watered the horses and cattle, then mixed up pig meal, I was sick with the cold and very close to tears.

We followed the cleared track across the slippery yard to the sound of mournful hens, and old Kubla Khan, the rooster, complaining that the ladies of his harem were being neglected and unfed.

"Breakfast first Jo," Dad decided, seeing that it was almost noon, instead of our usual time of a quarter to seven. Mum had stoked up the fire under her stock pot, and doled out enormous basins of thick, hot soup.

With snow falling from a sky the colour of an old floor cloth, we knew that our flock of ewes in lamb needed to be brought into the shelter of the barn, but first Dad had to dig a way to the fowl houses, while I continued to water the stock before the hole in the icy pond froze again.

Realising that the chicken's mash pail would be lighter for me to haul up from the pond, Dad had mixed the chicken food in the iron water bucket. I watched from the jetty as the hens took one look at the arctic conditions outside their warm fowl house, then retired back inside. Kubla Khan was much braver, but as roosters go, Kubla had a personality of his own.

Of Rhode Island Red stock, his mother must have mixed in some fine feathered company, for his colouring ranged from midnight blue and peacock green to all shades of brownish reds, black, white, and cream. He ruled his harem ruthlessly, and chased mice, rats, cats, and dogs. I watched him crow his defiance of the weather, then got on with my work, the chicken feed pail clattering as it hit the ice then went down into the pond.

Kubla Khan came rushing towards me, half flying, half running, wings flapping, hitting the frozen surface of the pond at speed. One moment there was a very surprised rooster skidding on his parsons nose, with his legs thrust inelegantly forward, then he simply vanished down the hole. I put out a hand to grab him but he disappeared, fluttering beneath the ice.

I slithered to the tool shed, grabbing an old sheep crook to puddle around in the water, but this proved futile. Dad brought a long ladder, crawling out along it as it lay across the pond. Elbow deep in the icy water, he tried to hook the crook round Kubla's neck or legs, and just when he was unable to bear the cold any longer, a few tail feathers came into sight. He hauled out the limp, wet, lifeless Kubla. Mum tried artificial respiration by the kitchen fire, but to no avail. She left the old bird lying in a state on the kitchen side table, saying that he might be as tough as old door hinges, but in this wintry weather, his carcase would work wonders for her stock pot.

With the snow storm assuming the proportions of a blizzard, we rounded up the sheep to safety, gave all our livestock double rations, littered them in deep straw, milked the cow early, and brought a plentiful supply of firewood inside the house.

The lamp was lit and the evening meal cooking before Mum had a chance to think about preparing Kubla Khan for cooking. She sat by the fire with the old rooster on her lap. As she tugged at the first few bedraggled feathers, one doleful eye opened, then slowly closed. Mum hesitated, knowing that fowls can run round flapping long after their necks are broken, but Kubla's eye blinked balefully again, then one sharp spurred claw twitched.

It was as if Mum was watching an old friend's resurrection.

She wrapped him in warm flannel, put him in a basket on the fender, poured neat brandy down his gullet and, by bedtime, we were sharing the hearthrug with an unsteady inebriated bird.

He was strutting around, chasing the cats from the kitchen first thing the next morning, so we took him to the fowl house for a frantically amorous reunion with his wives.

The bitter weather held, making caring for our livestock a nightmare, with every spare moment taken up with clearing snow. Unbelievably, the village postman struggled along the snow bound lanes to bring some Christmas mail. Pausing from pounding hot boiled potatoes into a warm oatmeal mash, Mum read a wistful message from a city dwelling friend.

"How happy you must be, making preparations for a white Christmas in the enchanting beauty of the snow covered countryside."

Mum chuckled as she read it. Applying dubbin to my snow saturated boots, I suggested that the word ecstatic more or less summed up my feelings on the subject.

"Humph!" my father grunted, shaking the paraffin drum to estimate if our supply of lighting fuel would hold out until road conditions allowed the oilman's van to get through to our cut off farmstead. "You can say that again!"

Miss Letty and the Sergeant

Shimmering through a mid-summer heat haze, the early morning sun infiltrated the closed upper window of Gunwanda Villa. Vaguely restless in her unruffled, virginal bed, Miss Letitia Pinke hesitated to get up and dress until "Matty Dear", her elder sister, called her. Matty Dear could get so irritable if anything disrupted the set pattern of their daily routine.

On bed-socked feet, creeping quietly to avoid the creaking of the uncovered floorboards, Miss Letty pulled back the long dark curtains and opened the windows. With her crocheted bed-shawl drawn close around her shoulders, she stood listening to the blackbird that, as chief chorister, was leading a chorus of birdsong in an anthem to the dawn. She knew he would be perched among the top branches of the garden elms that kept the South side of the house in shade all summer, and that during winter, when the gales made the high boughs creak and groan in protest, threatened to smash Gunwanda Villa.

In her interminable, eventless adult years Miss Letty had spent what seemed to have been a lifetime of hours watching the constantly changing country landscape framed by the full depth window. It was the one place in the house where she could call her dreams her own.

Dear Papa and Matty Dear had such dominant personalities that she sometimes felt like an insignificant daisy growing in the shade of two large sunflowers, folding her petals and sheltering in the sanctuary of this tiny bedroom in any domestic storm. For Dear Papa the "Last Post" had long since sounded. With his demise, Matty Dear seemed to have added most of his idiosyncrasies and military foibles to the ever-increasing number of her own.

In Miss Letty's boarding school days, when Dear Papa first bought this old country cottage, he named it Gunwanda Villa to commemorate some far-flung outpost of the Empire where he professed to have served as an army officer. The place was still full of foreign trophies and mementoes that Matty Dear insisted should not be moved. During the last months of Dear Papa's life, the entire household routine had hinged around a massive jigsaw puzzle the size of his study table.

Dear Papa assured his daughters that when all of the several thousand pieces were completed the finished picture of *The Royal Durbar At Delhi* would reveal him in full dress uniform standing close to the King and Queen.

Still as he left it, the unfinished puzzle stayed scattered on his table. Each day it was Lettie's task to dust it. After Dear Papa's death she would sometimes add a piece if she noticed where it would fit while she was dusting, but Matty Dear seemed to know if any piece had been moved. Matty Dear's moods of irritability had increased noticeably from the day they faced the distressing task of going through Dear Papa's personal papers after his funeral.

It was then that they realised that Dear Papa had journeyed abroad only in his imagination, for his military travels had taken him no farthest than Aldershot, and this as the lowliest grade of army clerk. They learned, too, that the mother neither remembered had not in fact been careless enough to become a

Bengal tiger's breakfast. She had obviously died in an influenza epidemic, and it was the money she left in trust for her daughters that gave them the meagre financial allotment on which they still lived. Matty Dear insisted that the truth must be their secret. They must keep up appearances at any cost.

Their frugal standard of living grew more spartan and, as the two women struggled to exist in the decaying old dwelling, anything that could not be mended without cost or paid assistance was left alone.

A damp patch, shaped like a map of Greenland, marred the whitewash of Miss Letty's bedroom ceiling. It extended its territory with every rain shower, but maiden lady daughters of a military gentleman could not lower their dignity to clamber up on the roof to mend the sagging roof timbers and slipping peg tiles, it was simply not *done*. Assured by her elder sister that the roof would outlast their lives, Miss Letty kept a bucket on her bedside rug, ready to catch the drips each time it rained.

But on a sunbright morning such as this Miss Letty could forget the draughty, damp discomfort of Gunwanda Villa in winter. Bees were working in the full-blooming honeysuckle covering the porch below her. Clematis and the pink Albertine roses that climbed unrestricted up to the bricks of the crumbling chimneys were heavy with flowers. Still wet with dew, they filled the air with a sweet-scented, almost tangible presence, and for one of the few times in her life Miss Letty felt happy with her existence in the rose-infested slum.

Across the lane, so close that she felt she could almost pick them, wild dog roses blossomed in the high hedge of the hayfield that a few days ago was a knee-high carpet of ox-eye daisies, mauve vetch, red sorrel and tall flowering grass.

All week long the field had echoed to the sound of agricultural activities. First, the clattering mowing machine drawn by two perspiring Shire horses cutting the grass and leaving it neat in patterned rows. There were old men with scythes, then women wielding wooden hayrakes and pitchforks, turning the drying hay and piling it into lumps. And all the time the happiness of their laughter seemed to taunt Letty, shut in as she was behind the bottlegreen roller blinds that Matty Dear insisted must be drawn to prevent dust and sunlight ruining the furnishings and all the valuable trophies Dear Papa had brought home.

The sun was gaining warmth with every moment and, knowing that Matty Dear would still be sleeping until the alarm clock Dear Papa had used throughout his military career woke her, Miss Letty let the woollen bed shawl drop from her shoulders, undid the top buttons of her high-necked nightdress, rolled up the sleeves and let the sunshine soak into her chest and arms. Warm and happy with this one small gesture of uninhibited freedom, she watched men from the farm across the meadows lead their Shire horse teams to pull the loaded haycarts that had stood overnight at the far side of the hayfield.

Someone was singing in a strong baritone voice that kept in rhythm with the lurching cart being hauled across the field. Unaware that she could be observed, Letty listened to the sound of the shod hooves in the lane, then watched the approaching cart slow and stop while the waggoner mended the trace horse's leading rein. The top of the load drew up directly in front of her bedroom window. And there, stretched out full-length, khaki-shirted, with a highly polished brass-buckled leather belt holding up his extremely scruffy grey flannel trousers, was a man. Not young, not old, but bronzed as if he made a habit of sunshine, and with a lot of crinkly lines around his eyes.

If he was surprised to see Miss Letty standing at her window with her hair loose around her shoulders and her white cotton nightie undone to the third button, Miss Letty was transfixed.

"And aren't you the most lovely sight in all this beautiful morning?"

For one moment Miss Letty thought he intended to leap across to the bedroom window, instead he leaned over and reached among the green foliage close by her, then handed her a half-open bud of a perfect Albertine rose.

Afraid to look into mocking eyes that must surely go with so cruel a jest, she held the rose as if it might shatter like a cobweb and thanked him for the gift. As the cart jolted into movement, she looked at the man on the hay load. There was nothing but gentleness and an inexplicable awe in his expressive eyes. "I'll be back," he called as the cart moved off.

At that moment she realised that Matty Dear was standing in the room. Matty marched across, hurled Miss Letty back on the bed, slammed the window and pulled the curtains to shut out the sun as if it were a *man*. For the next half-hour her behaviour and language were obscene.

Letty hid the rose under her mattress, and through the sameness of the day was forced to listen to a diatribe of hatred for a fool of thirty exposing herself to a common soldier who was home on leave farm labouring by day and carousing in the village inn by night.

The last of Miss Letty's evening tasks was to lock the back garden gate. That night she saw the sergeant standing waiting under the elms. He explained that his leave was almost ended, but he would like to write. For the first time it took a long time for Letty to lock the gate and, when she went indoors, her long hair hung around her shoulders like a girl's.

Matty Dear's barrage of sarcasm did not diminish with the passing weeks. Then one day, while Miss Letty was dusting Dear Papa's jigsaw puzzle, a letter arrived for her. It bore a foreign stamp. She read it, smiling, then deliberately swept every last piece of the jigsaw off the table and into the dustpan. Ignoring her sister's protests, she quietly went around the house raising the dark blinds, opening the windows and letting in the sun.

The Chinese Ghost

Like children enjoying the last game before bedtime, a gambol of lively lambs jumped and skipped, playing follow my leader around and over the trunk of a fallen elm that had lain uprooted since gales of winter flung it, groaning to the ground. Impatient, as all parents are when children remain energetically wakeful while their own eyelids feel lead-heavy, the old ewes ran towards them, calling, and stamping irritated hooves. One by one the romping lambs abandoned their game for their suppers, milk frothing around their mouths as they sucked noisily, their tails wriggling furiously, until, contented, they settled down to sleep.

Smaller lambs snuggled close to their thick-fleeced mothers, still overwhelmed by the wonder of being born. Their infantile bleating was answered with deep-throated maternal reassurances, and ruminating in-lamb ewes around them watched like well-meaning aunties offering advice.

Celandines, handfuls of small bright buttons made from pure sunlight at noontime, folded their petals as tendrils of cool mist haze, scented with wood smoke from some distant cottage chimney, drifted across the valley. In the duskiness of a still March evening a lone blackbird sang his requiem to the dying day.

One last look to make sure that no births were imminent then I could go home to the luxury of a book by the fireside.

A restless ewe, well away from the others and clearly in some discomfort, banished all hopes of such a pleasant hour or so. There were times when I envied those with the kind of nine to five occupations that allowed them to wear dancing slippers in the evenings instead of heavy farm shoes. Yet I knew that I could go to the ends of the earth searching and still find no place offering the peace of mind and contentment I had found in the few acres where, in grouchier moments, I could swear that I recognised every blade of grass.

I had no lantern with me and although the ewe had returned to her grazing I knew her lamb would arrive before daybreak, so I decided to go home for an hour then come back. During that hour ground mist had spread across the grass like a downy grey blanket, deadening the yellow light from the hurricane lantern I carried and making it difficult to count the slumbering flock. The ewe that I had specifically gone back to check on was close to where I had left her and was now the proud mother of a lamb. She stood licking it, encouraging it to rise on unsteady legs and stand beside her, but its first attempts to feed were rebuffed in her efforts to help its twin make a feet-first entry into the world.

This required assistance. Putting the first lamb close to the ewe's head to occupy her attention while I engaged in elementary obstetrics, I concentrated on the job of getting the second twin born. As soon as it began to breathe I laid it close to its mother's head, to join its brother, but the first lamb was not there. A new-born lamb cannot wander far of its own volition, and if it is lost it cries. The lantern was still where I first placed it, with the ewe well within the radius of its light. Convinced that I would still hear or see it, I searched in ever widening circles without finding a sign of the missing lamb.

I wandered around and around for what seemed like hours,

and by then another pair of twins and a single lamb had been born. These, carefully watched by their calling mothers, I shepherded into the warmth of the thatched shelters close by the gate. Watching the eddying mist rise and swirl like rippling waves at the ebb tide, I listened for the sound of a stray lamb crying, but all was silent, until I decided to do one more circuit of the field and began walking close by the hedge. At first I could hear a rustling behind me and was conscious of an unpleasant smell. I stopped. The noise stopped. I walked slowly, the rustling continued, and to my straining ears seemed to be coming from the far side of the hedge.

Reason tried to tell me it was one of Charlie Cartwright's grazing farm stock, attracted by the light. That theory leaked as surely as a rusty kettle, for I knew that the field had been sown with clover and had not had cattle on it since last year. If the unknown thing that was stalking me came through the hedge into Ten Acres I only had to turn round to find out what it was. I headed across the field toward the gateway, my imagination filling our quiet countryside with prowling leopards and wolves. Trying to lift my courage with the lantern, I turned around and where the bush of blackthorn makes the hedge lower saw the vague outline of something with hunched shoulders, standing six to seven feet tall, and with glowing eyes in a thin, pale, bearded face. The hurricane lantern flared, then dimmed, so I knew it was almost empty. I took to my heels and ran.

My father was coming across the orchard to see what had delayed me, and never was I more pleased to see the glow of his pipe. I told him about the lamb's disappearance and mentioned the rustlings in the hedge. The apparition was something different. Could you convince your father that you had just seen a seven foot ancient Chinese with amber eyes?

Dad thought that the lamb may have snuggled up to another ewe, and would be back with its mother by daylight, by which time I would be back out in Ten Acres acting midwife to the sheep. It was not there and one of the other twins that had been born the previous evening had disappeared as well. We realised then that any surviving pairs of lambs in our flock had been born during the daytime. If, as Dad suspected, a fox was lurking near the lamb pens, the ewes could defend one lamb but not two.

A couple of old doors, making a platform to stand on, were wedged into the branches of the fallen elm and the following evening we were both installed in a look-out made of straw bales. Dad had his double-barrelled shotgun with him and the loan of the village policeman's long-beamed torch. Windows across the valley darkened, a dog barked, someone cursed it, and a goat's incessant bleating suddenly stopped. A flight of lapwing, calling as they flew over, were invisible against the stars playing hide-and-seek among high clouds in the dark sky.

"There," said my father, pointing. The beam of the torch I was holding found what to me was just a shadow. My ears sang with the blast of a double report.

Scrambling down through the branches, we ran toward the thatched hurdles. There lay a very dead, very large dog fox. We walked around the startled flock until they settled, then went home to take the night chill from our bones with a warm fire and a bowl of Mum's thick soup.

A late caller arrived just as we started eating. The village policeman, having heard Dad fire, asked what he had shot. We told him and thanked him for the loan of the torch that had made it possible, but he brushed our thanks aside.

"Seems we've both had a successful evening, Harry. I caught that gippo chap from Pork Green tethering his old Billy for a bit of illicit night grazing on Cartwright's clover field."

Suddenly I could tell Dad about seeing the apparition. The *Thing* that had stood on its hind legs to glare at me over the hedge-top the previous evening was a smelly old goat.

Daily Deliveries Guaranteed

The Hare and Hounds marked the half-way stage of Dave's milk round so a midday pint for himself and a nosebag for his plodding pony were part of his normal routine. Each day the same old regulars congregated, sitting in their customary places, never varying in their habits until the day they greeted him with a handful of printed notices, each of them eagerly asking, "Ere, boy what do you think of these?"

Not too good at reading, Dave made the excuse that he had not brought his wife's glasses with him, and asked if the publican would mind reading the notice aloud: "Starting soon. Fresh milk twopence halfpenny a pint. Speedily delivered to your doorstep. Daily deliveries guaranteed."

While the landlord read the text of the notice twice for good measure, Dave pondered the implications of opposition that intended undercutting his prices by a halfpenny a pint. Anyone "speedily delivering" milk around the houses faster than his old pony would need to have a racehorse between the milk float shafts. No-one that the present company could think of had such an animal, but the publican was of the opinion that whoever was setting up in opposition to Dave intended to deliver milk by motor van or car.

Dave did not think that feasible. On our rough country roads milk shaken and bounced around in one of those infernal motors would be buttery and curdy by the time the churns were low and the milk round nearly done. Besides, who around here had a motor and the inclination to start up an opposition dairy round? At that time one could have counted all the car owners in the village on the fingers of one hand.

With the sense of hearing not then dulled by incessant noise and the ever increasing volume of traffic it was easy to differentiate between the individual sounds of local cars, and everyone would have known if a stranger was driving along our still quiet country lanes. The district nurse and the parson both drove venerable old Austin Sevens, yet their cars sounded completely different. The nurse subjected hers to the same hearty treatment she administered to hypochondriac patients, jollying it along with a stout-clad, accelerating foot.

The parson extended the same scant fervour to his driving as he did to his professed religion. The steepness of Lockley Hill invariably crept up on him like a sudden, unpleasant revelation.

No-one within a mile radius could fail to recognise the agonised, tooth-grinding groan of his car's gearbox undergoing torture. Neither nurse nor parson would be likely to start a pirate milk round. 'Nearly' Nigh, the publican's son, ran an old Vauxhall taxi, but he never reckoned to surface from bed before midday, so a milk round was the last thing he would want to own.

The gamekeeper's Trojan van pottered along like a rather breathless old spinster, unless it was chasing a gang of poachers, when it would snort along in pursuit, steamed up with indignation as if its modesty had been outraged. As His Lordship's employee, the gamekeeper was out of the running as a milkman. The only other car owner in the village was Jimmy Trott, a farmer. Dave knew that Jimmy's old bullnosed Morris had spent the early months of the summer out of action because Jimmy's barnyard geese had chosen to hatch out a clutch of eggs in it.

There was always the possibility that Jimmy might be considering milk production, but Dubber Walls vouched that the old Morris was greased and jacked up on old roof beams for the winter, its cylinder block and radiator guarded against freezing by the fact that it was buried under a ton of straw.

The only other regulars driving through our village were the paraffin chandler, the travelling draper and the vet. There were still those who believed that the 16 horsepower engine of the vet's Jowett had, in some mysterious way, retained an equine instinct that could find its way to any pub forecourt just as the bar doors were opening, and, by the same token, take its owner home safely at night. The Jowett's powers didn't run to doing a milk round without the cooperation of its owner, and milk was the last thing on earth he had any interest in.

The old men who watched the world go by from their perch on the forge yard wall were the first to notice the disreputable, rusty, overloaded tourer of mixed pedigree pass through the village, and by the time it had made its fourth return journey they were able to inform Dave that his rival intended to lodge with some smallholders over by Marsh Side, a hamlet eight miles distant. His plan was to collect surplus milk from farmers in the surrounding district and sell it in all the outlying hamlets on the way. He seemed a personable, cheerful young chap, dressed untidily, but with a touch of college learning about him, answering to the name of Miles. That was all we were ever to find out about him.

Dave, listening to the rattles, clanks and knocking of the rusty old car, decided he had nothing to fear. If the young man intended to try carrying full milk churns in that it would never get far from Marsh Side. It did though. Next morning Miles drove into the forge yard with ominous hammering noises coming from the car's internal regions. He asked Bert, the blacksmith, to strengthen it and put it right. Bert, inspecting the rusted running board and battered mudguards, said that it had restored his belief in miracles. It was not oil and petrol that had kept it running, but faith.

Enlisting the help of various bystanders, Bert put the car on its side, as if it were a thrown and hobbled mule, then fixed the loose and almost sheared couplings of its propshaft with four solid bolts. By the time he had strengthened the chassis and the bodywork, replaced rusted bonnet, mudguards and door panels with sheet metal and rust-protected it with green oxide, it looked more like a miniature Roman chariot than a car.

Bert even got the hood to move up and down, but that was a wasted effort, because within a few days of Miles starting his milk round it blew away and sank in Miller's Pond.

Miles's old car kept going, summer and winter, and even when our village was supposedly cut off by snow drifts Miles lived up to his original promise: 'Daily deliveries guaranteed.'

He had a ready wit, never lost for a reply to some tormenting old granny, but with a touch of chivalry about him, as witness his remark of "Sorry, mister," when he opened Tom Grommet's wash-house door to stand the milk out of the sunshine and caught Tom's wife taking a quick dip in the warm copper water suds. He kept his milk round going all through the middle and late 1930's, then just after the time of Dunkirk his customers found that one day their milk had been delivered long before they were up. Bert, whose forge was open at 6.30 every morning, was just in time to see Miles drive his old car into the forge yard. An Army jeep waited by Plough Lane corner.

Bert, as a World War 1 veteran, knew a military policeman when he saw one. Miles was being escorted away by two. Miles had left as mysteriously as he had arrived. Rumours ran riot. Some had him branded as a deserter from the regular army. Others were sure he was a secret agent for the allies, the enemy, or both. The folk he lodged with over at Marsh Side could throw no light on the subject.

One vague and uncertain clue came in the form of a newspaper photo which showed a group of commandoes embarking on a landing craft. With one exception all were grinning at the camera. The profile of this one soldier's face was remarkably like Miles.

Bert was sure that if he came through alive he would be back to claim the old car when the war was over, but it stood where he left it, enshrouded in bindweed and tall grasses until Bert and the forge itself had gone.

Shockodolly's Drains

I t was the nearest Harry Applethorn had ever been to striking, but no self-respecting waggoner could be expected to enjoy falling face-down in sticky clay twice in an hour, when he was supposed to be planting spring barley. He came stumping down the stable yard, looking like an unkilned toby jug, with both horses plastered to the hocks in mud. "The man ain't born as could make a fair old job of planting on the far side of Mockbeggar Field," he complained to my father. "'Tis like walking on half-cooked suet pudd'n when the water's gone off the boil in the pot. I ain't wasting my breath or breaking the horses' spirits stodging around up there."

"If you want it planted I reckon you'd better set to training they old crows to scratch around and sow a bit of seed. 'Tis certain sure they're the only things that won't sink in, for you'll not get it sown by anything with legs or wheels until it is properly drained."

Mockbeggar Field lies at the top of quite a steep bank, yet one half was always wet and extremely heavy to work. Given a warm dry spring, with planting conditions so good that we managed to get all the field sown at once, the seed on that side was always reluctant to germinate, remaining a month's growth behind the rest of the field, right through to reaping time.

It was one thing to recognise that it needed new drainage – finding the money to get it done was something else. Dad stood silent for a moment, as if he were weighing up the problem, then, serious-faced, replied. "If you think that rooks and crows are our only hope of planting Mockbeggar this year, Harry, how would it be if you helped me train 'em? With a bit of luck we might be able to teach them to line their nests with five pound notes. Doubtless we would both shin up the elm trees like schoolboys after eggs. That's the only way I can see me having cash to spare for miles of pipes, unless we're able to gather three harvests in one year."

The two men, friends as well as employer and employee, stood on opposite sides of the horse trough. Harry Applethorn grinned first. "You girt lummox," was all he answered, but both men understood that any anger had evaporated. "Reckon you could hand sow her, given a dry weekend, and if it's still too sticky for a horse harrow I could follow behind draggin' a hawthorn bough to cover it in."

A few days later I was dispatched in a hurry up to Mockbeggar Field with a jug of hot cocoa and two 'plate-pie-vittals' wrapped in tea towels for the two men's midday 'bait.' It was like stepping back into history, for men have sown and harrowed seed in the same way for at least two thousand years. My father, walking with easy strides, scattered seed from a hod hung around his neck to balance on one hip, while Harry Applethorn used a pair of crossed leather straps on his shoulders as a harness to haul a branch of a hawthorn tree to harrow in the corn.

The kidney-shaped seed hod, lip or maund, depending on the name each locality gives it, has remained unaltered through the years and some historians believe that the Maundy Money distributed by the reigning monarch on the day before Good Friday get its name from the maund, or pouch, used by the medieval kings to carry their largesse.

Promptly at noon both men stopped work. As I sat down with

them, waiting to take the empty jug and plates back home, three men who had been hedge cutting and ditching on Foxley Banks came across to join us. Each followed Dad's and Harry's example, folding an empty sack cornerwise to make a hood and protect their backs from the chill wind. What conversation there was centred on the sad and soggy condition of the tilth that side of Mockbeggar Field, although the hedge cutters were pretty monosyllabic, as if it cost them money to spare a word. The three bachelor Dann brothers were known as Ben, Treacle and Shockodolly.

In a family where thrift was a religion carried to fanatical extreme, Shockodolly's mop of snow-white hair grew far bushier than most before he would consider a fourpenny haircut to be financially worth while. A tall tale in the village held that Shockodolly's hair changed colour when he was young enough to enjoy Harvest Home. On such occasions it was the custom to pass around the hat for those who were sick or needing help.

Filled with free and unaccustomed beer, Shockodolly had recklessly put what he thought to be a penny in the hat, until the vicar made special mention of his philanthropy in so far as he had generously given a half-crown.

The story went that the thought of giving away almost half a day's wages turned his hair white with shock. True or not, the Dann family gave such junketings a wide berth after that year. In fact, they mixed with very few people at all, so that both Harry Applethorn and Dad were surprised when they came across Mockbeggar Field to spend their half hour dinner break. The hot bacon, onion and potato pasties were finished and the last of the cocoa generously shared between all five before Ben Dann got round to voicing the object of their visit.

"We did a bit of drain laying with our old chap when we were boys and we don't see why we couldn't get this 'ere water soaked away. It'd have a downhill fall. If its all right with you, we'll start on it first chance we get when the crop is off." Dad said he didn't think he could afford to pay for their labour and buy the pipes too.

"Pipes?" Shockodolly lifted the aged cap that lay on his head like a loose, mossy tile and scratched his scalp. "What'll we want pipes for when we can cut a hedge? We'll be over and make a start by the back end of the year."

They all stood up to go, but as Dad lit his pipe for a quiet smoke before he started work again Treacle took a clay pipe from his pocket and asked Dad for a match.

His tobacco smelled like nothing I had ever encountered before, and I said so. When they left, Harry Applethorn told me that the unique aroma was accountable to the fact that Treacle made his own smoking mixture of dried plantain, sainfoin leaves and a plant that grows on stagnant ponds.

That year went by, and so did the next. Mockbeggar Field still stayed muddy, although its draining was always going to be the Dann's next job. Ben Dann died suddenly, and that, Dad thought, was that, until Ada Dann met me in the village. At first glance she was a nondescript little woman with as much meat on her as a yard of pump water, and was about as colourful in character and dress. She only told me to have a load of straw bales ready in Mockbeggar Field the following morning, yet I could see why her brothers were loath to upset her.

Treacle and Shockodolly arrived at dawn with their new partner, a cousin who introduced himself as Nipper. As he made yards of straw rope with a hook and ratchet he said; "Poor old Ben, scrimping, saving, to put some money under the mattress, and all he got was a lumpy bed.

"Old Ada is so mean we only have one newspaper a week it's used as a table cloth, then torn into squares. She rations it out and gives us a piece at a time to take to the privy. If we don't need it we're supposed to bring it back. I saves mine up though, that fools 'er."

The Danns dug trenches, lining them with straw ropes and bundles of ash and hazel twigs. By the following spring Mockbeggar Field was drained enough for sowing to be over in time for Dad to plant potatoes before midday on Good Friday, thus adhering to an old country tradition known as planting at the foot of the cross. Nipper survived the Danns and had a whale of a time spending their hard-saved money. Now they have all become part of village history. But the straw rope drains they laid in Mockbeggar Field work on.

A Cushti Day

With the early-morning sun transforming the dew-damp grass into scintillating diamonds, I crushed a king's ransom of beauty with every step I took. From the encampment fire beneath the ripening cherry trees in the orchard, a tenuous wisp of blue smoke drifted lazily up into a sky as clear blue as a starling's egg. A broad-hipped Romany woman carrying a painted bucket to fill at the yard pump, acknowledged my "Good morning" with the prediction that the chance of riches would cross my path, and that for all of us it would be a *cushti* (good) day.

Lockley church clock striking half-past-six came clear across the still air as I walked to Barn Field to bring in the grazing horses; the sound of metal hammering metal echoed across the wooded valley from the village street. Bert, the blacksmith, was 'chiming the anvil' to announce the forge was open for business at the start of another country working day. Reluctant to leave their lush and shady pasture to be harnessed for working, the four horses continued munching, but Jim, the chestnut gelding, always inquisitive, every-ready for tit-bits and affection, ambled over to see what he could forage from my pocket. Cold bread pudding, carrots, apples, these were among his favourites, top rating being, without doubt a handful of potato crisps.

Happily quiescent as a contented baby, he stood with his chin resting on my shoulder as I slipped the rope halter over his head. Punch, the grey, was inclined to petulance, using heels and teeth if anyone upset him. The sight of Jim nuzzling around my pockets brought him at a full gallop toward me, a habit of his that looked terrifying to an onlooker, but I knew he would come to a sudden halt a few yards in front of me and stand whinnying, plainly asking for his share. Two haltered, two to catch.

Prince was a Suffolk Punch of doubtful ancestry, since he was a full 17½ hands high, had feet as big as meat plates, enormous strength and the obstinacy of a mule. He seemed to possess a fiendish sense of humour, taking the attitude; "So you think you will harness me for work when I could be grazing? Right then – first catch your horse." His one weakness was toffee, and if after a preliminary chase around the pasture I had still not managed to grab his mane and get him haltered a lump of toffee was my last resort.

Not that I dispensed these freely. At two old-fashioned pennies for a quarter pound they were too dear to lavish on a mule-headed, obstinate old horse.

Turpin was a different proposition altogether. A much later acquisition, this barrel-chested bay Welsh cob ignored all the undignified chasing, seemed impervious to blandishments and would continue grazing until the other three were haltered and heading for the gate. With an expression on his face as clear as words, he would trot over and fall in behind the others as if to say "You three off to work then? Wait for me."

That we always seemed to muster a motley crew of haymakers was really understandable when the more agile local casual workers could earn far more money with less effort picking fruit. This meant our labour force consisted of helpers too old, nervous or otherwise decrepit to climb ladders or work aloft. Surprisingly, five helpers were mustered in the yard to start work at seven that morning. One was old Jimmy Spit, whose predilection for chewing tobacco had brought expectoration to so fine an art that he had the reputation of being able to engulf a flying gnat in sudden death. Apart from this one failing and his disconcerting tendency to nod off into a deep sleep at the most inopportune moments, Jimmy's willingness to help was pure gold.

With twelve acres of hay fit to carry, Dad considered it unbelievably good fortune to be faced with the other four eager volunteers. Tolly Budd and his three hefty sons were thatchers and hay trussers, wielding the enormous hay-knives to cut the compressed hay out of the stacks during the winter months, in the days before all mowing grass was baled. They lived on a cold comfort kind of smallholding, neither Tolly nor any of his sons having been wed. Of late Tolly had let it be known that they were not averse to having a bit of female influence at their homestead. Not that they wanted the place to be lumbered up with a "passel of scritching and gossiping wimmin," but if a hard-working young woman would choose any one of them she would require no wages, but could look after them all.

This to Tolly was a serious proposition, and as they stood there eyeing me in much the same way as they would any livestock that might be available for purchase I had began to realise just why they had come. Dad knew my thoughts without my having to voice them, but he grinned back the unspoken reassurance that he would keep a careful watch on the situation. A shrug of his shoulders told me that with four chaps eager to show off their muscular charm for my benefit in our hayfield, this was far too good an opportunity to miss.

Luckily my first job was to drive Turpin to and fro with the lumbering hay rake, gathering the rows of dried grass into lumps. Jogging along with scented honeysuckle and sweet briar in the hedgerows, the air filled with bird song and the sun-warmed, sweet-smelling hay piling up behind me seemed to me to be as near to living in paradise as I could wish for. It was as the gipsy woman predicted, a cushti day. I had finished the raking by eleven, and joined the others loading the waggons or working on the stack. Jimmy Spit seemed quite agitated and at our midday break called me for a word in private on the far side of the stack.

"Can't think what Harry is up to. There's Tolly Budd saying

that Harry ought to begin thinking about getting you wed and off his hands, and Harry hinting that you had ideas along that road yourself. Don't you get mixed up in that rum lot, gal." For all that he chewed tobacco and was scruffy, Jimmy was a true friend, so I let him into a secret that the Budds did not know. Chuckling, he sat down under the ladder on the shady side of the haystack and promptly fell asleep. Although Dad and I had a packed meal with us I didn't fancy spending an hour being watched by a bevy of Budds, so I made an excuse that I was going to slip home.

Instead, I took my sandwiches to eat under the shade of the walnut tree on the edge of New Take orchard. The tree was loaded with green walnuts the size of pullet's eggs, just the right size for pickling. I asked one of the gipsy men if I could borrow a picking basket, and he volunteered to bring over a sixty stale ladder to put up into the tree. One of the gipsies, seeing the ladder empty took it away. For once I was glad to see Tolly and the youngest Budd approaching. I called down that I was stuck. Tolly summed up the situation. "Try walking about up there and you'll soon come down, gal," was all he said.

His son brought a ladder and stood at the bottom as I scrambled down. Paws, green teeth and perspiration, he attempted a passing peck, muttering in a fervour of thwarted passion: "Gor. You dun arf taste good." I ran.

Time to start work, I went around the stack to wake Jimmy. He lay snoring, his hat over his eyes, and just above him on the stale of the ladder a hanging, humming, heaving swarm of bees. Tolly thought we might shake them into one of the horses nosebags, but it seemed too risky. I was dispatched to find the lady bee-keeper over at Penny Pot Lane.

The Budds and Dad would continue to load the waggons, leaving Jimmy to sleep on if he could. It so happened that the lady apiarist was out chasing the swarm. Jimmy woke to find her hooded and netted bending over him. He thought his end had come, but saw nothing remarkable in not being stung. "You chew tobacco, girl, and nothing'll pester you." That I could well believe.

The hayfield was cleared and stacked by evening. When the Budds collected their pay Tolly again raised the question of my getting married and off Dad's hands. Only then did Dad inform him that my banns of marriage to the blacksmith's son had been called in church that week.

As we turned the tired horses out to graze, the gipsy woman called: "Cushti evening, Guv." "Cushti," we replied – and meant it, too.

The Conservationists

Conservation was not a word much used in the days when Jack helped us with sheep dipping, cleaning cattle yards, muck spreading and the more disagreeable jobs that took more muscle power than Dad and I could muster on our own. If anyone had called Jack a supreme conservationist, his denial would have been forthright and probably unprintable, him having no inclination for fancy phrases or long words.

Despite his obvious willingness and ability, the local landowners were reluctant to employ him. His dishevelled appearance and aversion to soap and water put them off. We could not afford to be so fussy, and in accepting Jack's enthusiastic help we had to accept his shortcomings as well.

True, we did try to nudge him into more hygienic standards, but tactful hints that his social habits left much to be desired were as effective as trying to break up concrete with a pin.

Dad spoke plainly. "Good God, Jack. The last time I whiffed anything to equal you was when that old ewe went missing for a fortnight and I found her drowned and rotting in the dyke."

Such pointed insults scarcely scratched the surface of Jack's finer feelings beyond the instant retort of "Yus. And wouldn't the silly old mutton head 'ave still been alive and kicking if 'er 'adn't ventured to put her hooves in water. Didn't do 'er no good. Nor would it me."

In a village where mains water was still a council election promise, where sink and bath tub taps only functioned in those households affluent enough to engage someone to pump well-water up into overhead tanks, we learned young the true value of the wells and springs around us. Every dwelling had its water butt for catching rain.

There were advantages since there was, and still is, nothing to match rain water for making hair soft, silky and shining, with the minimum of fuss and shampoo. It was the one concession to beautifying that the most straitlaced and narrow-minded matrons would allow, and the clear smooth complexions for which country girls were once noted owed much to the old water butt by every back door.

Water snails and fat yellow-bellied slugs that were sometimes hauled up from the depths of the well in the huge elm-wood buckets were regarded as proof that the water was pure and proud we were, too, of its clear clean taste. All of us except Jack. He reckoned that if we had been meant to drink water from buckets we would have come on this earth equipped with necks the same shape as a horse.

Of course, he drank it indirectly, keeping a battered enamel teapot constantly brewing on the hob of his cottage range. Lined with a thick coat of tannin that would have stiffened leather, this was topped up each morning with water and a fresh pinch of tea.

By the weekend there were more leaves than liquid, but each Sunday morning Jack would empty the pot, carefully straining off the leaves to dry them on an old tin tray in the oven. Mixed together with the contents of his tobacco tin, Jack knew how to make half an ounce of shag last a very long time indeed.

As I said, Jack was a model conservationist after his own fashion, so thrifty that he would transform the roadside nettles into a passable home-brewed beer to supplement tea. For years he lived a solitary bachelor existence but when his cousin died, leaving a widow penniless in a tied farm cottage, Jack offered her the shelter of his home.

Old Lou's arrival as Jack's housekeeper gave those who were intrigued by his way of life the opportunity to seek verification as to whether he did, or did not, wear his wellies in bed.

He made no secret of the fact that, come winter or summer, he never shed shirt, pants or hat at bedtime, saying that, "When horses, cattle and rabbits take their coats off at night, so will I."

Timorous as a skinny, ageing squirrel, old Lou was too grateful that Jack had let her retain some measure of independence to have discussed his sleeping habits with anyone. She asked little except that she be allowed to rest on the broken-springed old sofa in the kitchen when her day's work was done.

Simple, economically minded, her standard of living was as frugal as Jack's, although she was somewhat more hygienic, and nothing that went into that cottage was wasted, nothing was thrown away.

Jack would never leave a piece of wood that would feed his kitchen stove and, in turn, the wood ash was emptied on the garden to fine down the soil. He grew some marvellous crops that never wilted in dry weather, because the well water that Lou used went, via the dish pan, back into the soil.

Table scraps, peelings and wild seeds helped to feed the chicken at the bottom of Jack's garden. Even the few tins that were used were cut open, flattened and nailed like slates or tiles around the hen house walls to keep it snug and dry.

Jack collected or cadged any garden seeds he noticed, and these would be hung up in unlabelled paper bags on the innumerable nails and hooks that covered the ceiling of the kitchen. This could sometimes lead to slight misunderstandings and mistakes, such as the time that Lou, acting on the kindest of intentions, administered a brew of the silvery dried 'Honesty' seeds instead of Senna pods when Jack's stomach was upset.

Lou collected sheep wool from the hedgerows, washing it and making it into the padding for warm patchwork quilts. She would collect the bundles of binder twine that used to clutter up the farm barns after threshing time, plaiting and stitching it into mats. Despite her ministrations, Jack continued to resemble a walking straw stack. It took desperate situations to make him even consider replacing his worn-out clothes. I remember the year that the seat of his trousers was so threadbare that total disintegration was simply a matter of time. Dad and I had private wagers on the limit of their survival. "Tomorrow, the weekend, next week—," but we had not reckoned on Lou's ingenuity. Just when Jack was obviously due for an embarrassing predicament, he came to work with the hole in his trousers cobbled together with massive stitches that had been sewn with a sacking needle threaded with binder twine.

That day Jack was pulling mangolds, taking the leaves off and piling them up in lumps. I was loading them on to the trailer of my old tractor and hauling them into the frostfree shelter of the barn. I noticed that each time I passed by that morning he looked discomforted and purple faced beneath the top dirt and the stubble of his beard. At last he came trotting over and asked where Dad was. He had to see him "confidential-like and quick." I knew that Dad was with a sow that was farrowing in the pigsties. "For pity's sake then, gal, drive me up there quick."

I didn't hang about. Nor would you with Jack close beside you on the tractor, and his face looking more pained and purple all the time. Dad, hearing the tractor, came out to see what was the matter. Jack leapt down and dashed toward him. "Quick, Harry, get out your shut-knife and come into the barn to help me." Dad stood still, more than a mite puzzled. "Don't stand there asking fool questions. I'm desperate. There I was, quietly behind the hedge and settling down nicely to drop my tailboard to answer a call of nature when I realised that Lou, silly old besom, stitched up more than she ought when she mended up my breeches. The blamed things won't part company with my shirt!"

Dad emerged from the barn, Jack following some minutes later. He clutched a corn sack coyly around his middle. I was despatched to ask Mum for an old pair of my father's trousers. We rummaged around in the old wooden box known as our hope chest, since we dumped discarded garments in it, hoping that they would prove useful later on. We found a rough pair of old corduroys with more patch than leg to them. Dad was much taller than Jack, but this worried Jack not a bit. Standing in the middle of the yard, he put them on over his worn ones, tucking the spare into his wellies and commenting that they would keep him warm a treat.

Now when every section of the media entreats us to save water, energy and fuel, I remember Jack. If that true master of conservation could have been around to lecture folk on the subject he would have earned a lot more money than he got by dipping sheep or pulling mangold-wurzels with us.

Someone's Pet

Sunshine and drying March winds made planting conditions perfect for me to tractor harrow the ploughed furrows to let Dad sow barley with his old-fashioned two horse drill. We worked until it grew too dark for Dad to follow the line of the drill marks, then he led his tired team back to the stables while I sheeted up the old tractor under the larch row fringing Parsons Wood. A chill dampness had descended with twilight, and an unfelt breeze that sighed among the tree tops made me shiver as I walked along the edge of the lambing pasture on my way back home. The cracking of twigs and a movement in the wood startled me until I recognised one of the estate game-keepers emerging through the trees. He called out, warning me that a couple of sheep worrying dogs had attacked his foster hens raising clutches of young pheasants in his rearing pens just beyond our boundary fence. The local policeman had given him the description of the dogs as being a black and tan collie and a smaller black mongrel, along with permission to shoot either dog on sight.

Our lambing season was almost at an end, the fine weather working wonders for the mothers and their babies, and as I walked home in the deepening gloom, all the ewes were placidly chewing the cud, with their lambs snuggled close to their fleece for the night.

Mum was anxious to get breakfast cleared early the next morning, for Spring to Mum meant chick rearing, and with several of her hens already going broody, she intended to transform apple boxes and chicken wire into maternity coops for fowls. Leaving Dad to tackle the essential farm chores, before he brought a load of seed corn down the field to start drilling, I went on ahead to count the sheep and see if the last few barren ewes had achieved unlikely motherhood, then start harrowing to get the soil ready for the seed drill.

Watching rooks and pigeons clustering around our fields in anticipation of an easy breakfast, I took the old single barrel shot gun and bird scaring cartridges to persuade them to move on. My footsteps left a distinct trail in the dewy grass, but other tracks criss-crossed them and when I reached the lambing pasture, the flock was in one corner, panting and wild-eyed.

I stayed to calm them, but there was ploughed land waiting to be planted, so all I could do was keep an eye on them each time I took the tractor and harrow to the top end of the field.

'Florrie Fordson' was sometimes temperamental when I tried to overwork her. That morning she sulked, coughed and spluttered every time she met rough going and, soon after Dad began drilling, she misfired and stopped. As I took a spanner to her filter, I heard a commotion coming from the direction of our yard. A dog was barking, chickens squawking, then I heard the unmistakable sound of the stableyard bell. This was Mum's recognised emergency signal, only rung when she needed urgent help.

Dad could not quickly leave his horses so, grabbing the rook gun and a few cartridges, I raced across the field. As I ran I saw two dogs running in the lambing pasture, advancing on the terrified sheep. Ears flat to his head and half crouching, the collie circled the flock, but the little black mongrel tore in among them snapping at the fleeing lambs. He caught one by the back legs the collie coming to join him, grabbing the lamb's head in a macabre tug of war. I had been midwife to the flock, knowing each by sight and name.

Trembling with fury, I loaded the gun as I scrambled through the hedge, oblivious to the thorns that lacerated my clothes and arms. By that time the lamb had been decapitated, the collie seeking further sport, but the black mongrel lingered to play with the headless body, heaving it in the air like a rag doll. Knowing that the cartridges were only powder and wadding, I was so raging angry that I aimed for the mongrel's head. The old gun had a kick like a stallion thumping my shoulder and seemed to make a double report.

The collie had vanished by the time my eyes would focus properly, but the mongrel lay inert beside its victim. I ran over to it, wondering how a badly aimed blank cartridge fired at a distance could knock it out cold, then realised that it had been shot in the head. Another shot reverberated across the fields, but I was in no state to recognise if it was Dad's twelve bore. I only knew that I had actually killed in anger for the first time in my life. A tag on the dog's collar gave it the name of 'Blackie', and I realised that I had probably shot someone's pet.

The persistent ringing of the stableyard bell brought me to my senses so I left the dog lying, counting three dead lambs and a savaged ewe as I ran.

I found Mum hysterically tugging at the bell rope, blood pouring from her arm. Sobbing, she said that she had been collecting a broody hen from the nest boxes in the fowl run when the two dogs dashed through the unlatched gate. They had killed and savaged several hens before she could drive them off, but the collie had turned on her, flying for her throat. Protecting herself by covering her face with her hands, it had bitten her arm instead. She was in a state of shock, needing more than iodine to treat her injuries. Dad brought the two horses into the yard at the trot, we harnessed one to a tip cart and I drove Mum to the casualty department of the hospital in town.

The overwhelming anger I had felt in the lambing pasture welled up again, watching my trembling mother, I wished that the owners of the dogs could have the carcases of our tortured animals dumped in their own back yards. While I waited for Mum outside the hospital, for there were no facilities to park a tip cart, I realised that the address on the dead mongrel's collar was a side turning off that street.

Leading the horse down a narrow entry that was sunless, drab and smelly, I hammered on the appropriate door, determined to say my piece. There were sounds of movement behind the paint-starved panels, but whoever was answering my knock was taking their time. All my anger evaporated as the door slowly opened to reveal a tiny, shrunken old lady, crippled with arthritis, supporting herself with a stick. She smiled a quavering welcome, thinking I was the daughter of a man who went round the streets selling bundles of logs. I tried to explain, but she continued talking in a confused fashion, saying that she could not afford more than a tanner's worth if I was charging sixpence a bundle. She spoke so quickly, I could only stand and listen to her saying that I was the first soul she had spoken to for days. Praying I had come to the wrong house, I eventually managed to ask her if she had a dog called Blackie.

"Blackie?" Her face lit up with the warmth of affection. "He's my little baby! Has he been showing off his tricks to you then, bless him? My late husband taught him to do all manner of nonsense like playing hide and seek with dog biscuits, or pretending to die for the king. He knows every word I say, does Blackie. Now I'm alone and so tottery that I can't get out of the house, he's all I have left."

She looked so frail, so unloved, so poverty-stricken, I could not bring myself to tell her that I had shot her dog. All I could do was burst into stupid snivelling tears and break the news that Blackie was lying dead in a country meadow. At this point Mum came along. She had seen the horse and cart in the entry and, taking immediate grasp of the situation, backed me in my white lie.

"An accident?" the old lady sobbed, tears coursing down her grey cheeks. "My poor little boy did so love a run in the park, he would have loved being in the country. Did he follow someone out there? Will you see he is properly buried there?" We left her with the illusions about her dear little pet and headed for home.

On the way back, we met the village policeman. He looked

with concern at Mum's bandaged arm. Before I could admit to him that I had shot the black mongrel, he said, "You know the game keeper has killed both of the sheep killers, don't you? He said he was afraid you would fire that old rook gun before he could get a shot at the small black dog, but he beat you to it by a fraction of a second. The collie he got at point blank range. That pair accounted for at least sixty head of stock between them. Your evidence will get us a couple of convictions when we put the owners in court."

Thinking of that sad, housebound old cripple, Mum said there was no point in threatening a prosecution. Putting the poor old soul in court would not bring sheep, lambs, or chicken back to life. All she wanted to do was to get home and get on with making hen coops for the baby chicks that would soon be hatching. I had an appointment with a temperamental tractor, trying to make up for lost time to help Dad plant seed barley.

The Antagonists

A skilled craftsman, making ashwood fruit-picking ladders all winter, Joe Sprockett's summer inclination was to work in various farm orchards, moving ladders from tree to tree for those who picked the apples, cherries, pears and plums. Happily content to set up a makeshift warm-weather home in some disused chicken ark or cattle shed, bachelor Joe's mode of life was regarded as a family disgrace by his sister-in-law, Emma, who lost no opportunity to air her vituperative views.

No love was lost between Joe, nearly sixty, and his brother's widow, a lady of uncertain age. Waging continuous verbal battle, Joe did nothing to disprove the village stories circulating after the Monday morning when his brother, Sam Sprockett, breathed his last.

Sam made an unfortunate, unexpected exit from this vale of

trouble beneath an overturned manure cart. That a carelessly replaced cotter-bar of a dung cart would change her status from wife to widow seemed to Emma typical of Sam's contrariness. It irritated her that Sam should create a crisis when her copper chimney was drawing well and heating water quickly, and this on the first fine warm Monday washing morning there had been for months.

Joe Sprockett's antagonism towards his sister-in-law rose to explosive proportions when, in company with three other shocked and white-faced farmhands, he carried the victim home. To have taken Sam to the parish mortuary involved a two-mile trudge, notwithstanding the fact that the small stone building by the churchyard had long served as the grave-diggers' tool shed and a store for the parson's logwood supply of winter fuel, so there would have been no room to lay Sam out. In any case poor Sam was smelling none to pleasant, so the perspiring quartet took him to his cottage to clean him up.

Emma refused to let them carry the hurdle-gate borne load over the threshold, peremptorily ordering them to lug their pathetic burden down-wind of her washing line. Given time to finish her laundering properly, she offered to provide a copper full of hot soapy suds for Joe and his helper to wash her late and less than sweet scented husband in the back yard, suggesting that while they were busy with bass brooms and buckets they could well scrub the yard. She thought it a terrible pity to let good hot water go to waste. Joe complained that after all the muck and manure his late brother has succumbed to, this was the last straw.

Harsh words and insults flew like missiles between Sam's two sole surviving family mourners and for all Emma's caustic tongue, interested onlookers thought Joe's observations at the funeral won him the contest of words, game set and match. To the parson, commiserating on the sad loss of his brother, Joe said:

"I don't think old Sam would reckon much on me a-grieving on him when he be tucked in down there snug, quiet and peaceful, out of old Emma's earshot. He had a smile on his face, and I ain't seen him look so happy since before the day she told 'un she'd decided they must get wed."

Regarded by most as being middling uppity and having ideas above her husband's wage packet, village curiosity questioned

how Emma would react to having no income at all. Joe's offer
of financial assistance was met with icy rejection as Emma chose
to retire behind the drawn blinds of Woodbine Cottage.

Apart from Short-foot Price, the travelling draper bringing
mourning clothes on approval, and a smartly dressed insurance
man from the city, there were few to whom Emma's door was
open.

Bothered by a sense of brotherly duty, Joe Sprockett wondered
if Sam's widow might be penniless but too proud to admit it.
The situation was not improved when he heard that she had
somehow found the money to buy her house. Woodbine Cottage
became Wood Villa, and an advertisement in the local weekly
paper announced that Mrs. Sam Sprockett was offering the
hospitality of her country residence to suitable and impeccably
referenced guests.

Puzzling aloud how Emma had achieved such a financial
miracle, Joe was enlightened by the post-mistress who informed
him that for several years Emma had paid hefty insurance pre-
miums on both Sam's life and his own. The news gave Joe an
uneasy, cold sensation that ran from the region of his back collar
stud down to his twitching toes.

Emma's only guest proved to be the smooth-talking insurance
man from the city. The downstairs front room became his bedsit-
office, complete with typewriter and filing cabinet. It did wonders
for Emma's ego to tell callers clutching insurance books, "My
guest is in his office. I will ascertain if he can be disturbed."

It was a thought to treasure that she alone in all the village
sat down to meals with a shaven, shiny-shoed man wearing a
clean celluloid collar and a blue serge suit. Joe, who still kept
the hedges clipped and the garden tidy, called her a daft old
besom to make sheep's eyes and act dotty over some rent-paying
tame insurance man.

Short-foot Price was allowed to take a cup of tea in the
kitchen when he called every Thursday, and while Emma
Sprockett could hardly have been said to encourage visitors, it
seemed for a while that her caustic temperament had begun to
lose some of its sting. This state of affairs faded when her lodger
started rushing through his tea to don cycle clips and bowler
hat, then go pedalling down the lane. He was reticent about

these nightly excursions, frequently returning with cement dust, paint and distemper on his boots.

Emma confided he suspicions to Short-foot. With every local birth, wedding or death providing his drapery round with potential profit, Short-foot made it his business to investigate. It sounded as if old Emma's lodger was setting up home elsewhere, probably needing household linens. It was in his own interest to find out.

On his next drapery round day, Short-foot imparted the news that the insurance man was courting a kennelmaid from Foxley and renovating an old cottage out that way.

"Of course," said Short-foot astutely, "these young women wear different clothes that make them look slimmer and more attractive than more matronly ladies."

With a sour expression, Emma asked him to explain.

Fetching a box from his van he held up a type of corsetry she had always favoured. Strong sludge grey cotton, supported by fearsomely stiff whale boning, it was beset with eyelet holes and yards of stay lace, looking less like a garment than a barricade. Short-foot then offered a small tubular garment for her inspection, but taking it for some sort of elasticated stocking, Emma said she wasn't fretted over the shape of her knees.

"Dear Lady," said Short-foot, the super salesman. "These are the height of fashion in upper-class circles, guaranteed to hold upward and inward all that has sagged or spread. It is called a roll-on corselette."

He suggested he might leave the garment for Emma to try on in the privacy of her bedroom, then she could pay for it when he came round again.

After a tea of cold kippers and icy disdain, Emma's lodger went to his room to get ready to meet his loved one as his landlady stalked haughtily up the stairs, some moments later he heard strange bumping sounds coming from her bedroom, followed by a strangled kind of groan. He went up the stairs, knocked on the door, but found it locked. Cycling off for help, he met Joe Sprockett who collected one of his fruit-picking ladders and leaned it against Emma's bedroom window sill.

Wasting no time with formalities, Joe clambered up and into Emma's bedroom to find her clad only in sleeved vest and knee-length fleecy-lined bloomers. The roll-on girdle like an updated strait-jacket was imprisoning her chest, upstretched arm and head. On the top of the ladder, the lodger leaned on the window sill, laughing loudly, saying that his girl friend always put her feet into a similar garment, then hauled it up. Joe dispatched him to the kitchen to fetch a carving knife to cut Emma free.

Almost hysterical she called out. "Who is to pay for this Joe Sprockett? How can I explain to Short-foot Price that you have climbed into my bedroom and hacked his elastic corset to pieces while I was trying it on!"

"Me, I reckon!" Joe said, trying to calm her. "Get yourself dressed decent. We could both do with a cup of tea."

Emma sat in the kitchen, flushed and embarrassed by her ordeal.

"What did you want to squeeze into that thing for, you silly old besom?" Joe said, smiling. "If its company you want, I need someone to look after me a bit during the winter. I know that folk reckon you take a rasp to your tongue to keep it so sharp, but you ain't bad looking under your burrs and prickles, and I do enjoy a good old argufying fight."

Emma Sprockett, sitting beside him drank her tea, uttering not one word.

Queen Ethel Who?

The Parsonage Garden Party had always been a select affair, patronised by the more affluent parishioners who were too refined to expect anything more from the price of entry than to have the right to take stewed tea and stale scones on the ant infested lawn beneath the cedar, or browse among the articles for sale on a flag draped table on the terrace in front of the house. Penny glasses of powdery lemonade were provided for small fry brought unwillingly by mind-your-manners mothers, as were tuppenny dips in tubs of bran.

It was always hinted that a golden sovereign was hidden among the paper wrapped gobstoppers, marbles, liquorice bootlaces and penny whistles, but no one ever found it, and the Doubting Thomas element in the village questioned the existence of such mythical wealth. At an exorbitant half a crown to get past the Parsonage gate posts, those who knew their place in the social pecking order of the parish, regarded 'parson's party' as an uppity annual non-event.

That year the parson was forced to the conclusion that while he deplored the lowering of social barriers, he must widen the scope of the occasion to ease a pressing financial need.

All due respects to the ladies of the Busy Bee's Sewing Circle, but if every knitted egg cosy, embroidered chair back and stitched hot bottle cover was snatched up, there was no hope that their price would raise one fiftieth of the filthy lucre he must find.

The church roof timbers were plagued with an infestation of beetles and, closer home, wet rot was crumbling the floorboards in the parsonage scullery and bathroom, causing an embarrassing situation he hesitated to discuss publicly.

Shunning pleasures of the flesh, he favoured the early morning cold water scrub routine of bathing, but his spinster sister was made of weaker stuff. She tended to stoke the kitchen back boiler until the pipes vibrated then indulge herself in a twice weekly soak, chin deep in a decadent, huge, hot bath. Her weight, combined with that of the brimming iron bath tub, had eventually proved too much for the floor joists. Hearing her screams from behind the locked bathroom door, he had been obliged to enlist the blacksmith's help to get in and help her out. The spectacle that had confronted them after the blacksmith had forced the door with a crowbar, was one he would have difficulty in eradicating from his mind.

While the bung hole of the bath had stayed firm, the top end had fallen through the floorboards, lodging at an angle. Head down, feet threshing the air, his solidly-built sister was trapped, made more hysterical by the fact that a cold water pipe had fractured and was showering her with spray. Eyes averted, using the bath mat to cover the victim's confusion, it had taken all of the blacksmith's muscular effort and the parson's own words of encouragement to haul her out.

In beseeching the blacksmith to maintain a discreet silence about the incident, the parson stressed how urgent a new and massive repair fund had become and how few were his hopes of success. Never one to mince his words, the blacksmith suggested that the garden party be enlarged and made more attractive to ordinary village folk. Democratically the parson put up several notices asking for suggestions. Any ideas thus offered would be discussed at a village meeting. No workable scheme would be refused.

The notice began: "Our village church has seen a thousand years of history . . ." Of such words are inspirations made. If this was so, why did we not stage a celebratory gala instead of the usual garden party? We could perform a pageant or some similar spectacle.

This idea was backed up by the new and still enthusiastic schoolmaster who had found some ancient local history books. It was agreed that this could be planned and the scenario written, subject to the parson's approval. Suggestions poured in, some feasible, some not.

One so approved was grass-track cycling, or even motor-cycle races around the parsonage paddock, the proviso being that the four acres of waist-high docks, thistles and couch-grass be mown and cleared without charge to the parson. There were to be bookstalls, white elephants and the less dignified rummage. Prompted by his privately-tippling sister, the parson even consented to a bring-and-buy bottle stall, as long as she was in sole charge.

At one time, before it was hauled off to the city as tourist bait, there was a ducking stool at a village along the river in which scolds and nagging shrews were dunked in the water. Someone suggested that Old Humph, the wheelwright, make a replica, for there were several men who would gladly pay to see it used. Old Amos, the horse-dealer and a betting man, offered to put a subscribed stake on a dead-cert dark horse he was backing, thus dispensing with any need for a gala, but this the parson overruled.

Meanwhile, the process of delving into local history made it plain that the village forbears were a pretty rough unpatriotic lot. Admitted, when Queen Ethelburga's horse dropped dead beneath her as she travelled along the wooded terrain on the edge of our parish, the locals made a rough litter and carried her on her way. That was an episode easily enacted, except that we could foresee problems in trying to find a co-operative horse. Seeing that our local Lordship and his Lady always patronised the Parson's Garden Party with a donation rather than their presence, we wondered if a scene depicting the first of the noble line earning his title might bring them to grace our gala day.

Research showed that the personal services to the Monarch that brought such grace and favour had been rendered by his illustrious ancestor's lady wife. In the circumstances we thought it better to leave that dusty bit of history unstirred.

Working in conjunction with the coastal marsh villages, running an escape route for French prisoners of war incarcerated in the hulk ships out in the estuary, was a remunerative source of income around abut the 1800's. There had to be a story there.

A villager had once been hanged for sheep rustling; then there was the girl who swore that visions and unseen voices had asked her to send messages to some very affluent people. The proof of her integrity was that she became instantly bed-bound and turned black. She fooled folk for years, too. Long before the Tolpuddle farmhands raised their voices our local lads were marching from farm to farm in protest at the new threshing machines that had robbed them of their winter task of flailing corn in the barns. Faced with starvation, they made their pathetic gesture, their banner being a loaf impaled on the prongs of a pitchfork, their cry of battle being, "Give us bread."

All in all, we were proud to hand our finished script to the parson. "Ah yes," he said. "There might be one or two small alterations, but I do see the stature of Queen Ethelburga in the blacksmith's wife." "Queen Ethel who?" was that lady's immediate reaction but she consented, and that scene alone was all that was regarded as suitable from our script. Considered far too radical and reactionary in outlook, 'The Enduring Forest' became 'Our Glorious Land.'

Drake played bowls on the parsonage lawn, Stanley met Livingstone, but somehow it was not the same. The funds raised just about patched the floor in the parsonage bathroom, and Old Amos added the final touch to the futility of the effort. As he told the parson, it was a pity that no one would listen to his offer. His dark horse had romped home, first past the post at odds of 100–1.

The Leaning Post

For years the latch post of Barn Field gate had rocked back and forth like a loose tooth every time the gate was opened. Replacing it was a task Dad always planned to do, "come the slack time after harvest," but time, like money, always seemed to be in short supply.

On the day that I misjudged the width of the trailer I was towing behind the cleat wheeled old tractor, thus flattening the gate post, Dad and Jimmy Spit were riding along deep in agricultural conversation, their legs dangling over the back of the trailer, until its iron banded wheel nave hit the gate post. Simultaneously both shot off and sat down hard on the ground.

"Bloody speed crazy, these young 'uns," Jimmy swore, complaining that he had just swallowed a whole new plug of chewing tobacco. I tried to explain that with a light load and a downhill gradient, I had been trying to alleviate 'Florrie Fordson's' sluggish performance which always affected her like chronic constipation if she had been subjected to a long period of slow heavy field work. In top gear, with the hand throttle pulled out to the last notch, this had seemed an ideal opportunity to give old Florrie her head.

This may have helped her internal workings but did nothing to diminish Dad's dislike of a mechanical contrivance incapable of being halted with a hollered "Whoa!" To be hurtled along by a speed-mad daughter at ten miles an hour could be stoically endured, but to clumsily clobber the gate post was something else. His dignity had collected as many bruises as his backside, so he was scathing in his comments.

"I teach you all I know, and you still know nothing! How many times have you been told you will never hit a gate post if your horse's nose is pointing straight down the middle of the track."

I pointed out that Florrie Fordson was without a nasal organ, but this remark collected all the contempt it deserved. I acknowledged that I had been distracted by the clusters of bright orange rowan berries covering the tree by the gateway, for they bore a remarkable resemblance to the decorations on my mother's refurbished felt hat. That too was adored with innumerable droplets of coloured sealing wax, in defiance of war time drabness.

Like Mum's hat the rowan tree was old, but provided a wide canopy of shade. Long years before someone had hung an iron 'S' hook in a low branch. The tree's defiant bark had all but engulfed the top half, but time-honoured custom decreed this to be the place to hang our dinner baskets and bags of food. Our food had come through the jolting undamaged but Jimmy Spit was more concerned about the two-gallon stone jar he had been holding steady in the back of the trailer. Like him, it had landed in the dust.

A protecting worm-eaten wickerwork basket had kept it unbroken, and I said so when Jimmy started to complain about good beer being spoilt.

"Book learning don't teach young 'uns that home-brewed beer needs to be kept quiet if it is to put starch in a working man's backbone. Mad beer, shook up like this, will just tie my chitterlings up in knots.'

We put the stone jar in the deep green shade beneath the rowan tree, piling corn sheaves around it to keep it cool and settle itself to rights. A few hefty stones rammed down into the post hole made the latch post straighter than it had been before.

With the two men opting to walk rather than ride up the field to start loading wheat, I drove along the field edge, wondering what good-intentioned soul had planted all the wild fruit in the hedgerow. There were wild damsons, codlin apples and yellow bullace plums along with the rowans. Strict wartime sugar rationing prevented jam-making, but my Mum preserved them just the same. When all preserving jars were full she used jam jars, topping each one with a thick layer of melted mutton fat.

Swarms of wasps and hornets were gorging themselves on the ripe damsons and hollowing out the codlin apples. They were more ready for picking, but being so short-handed, all we wanted was time. The trees were old and spindly, liable to snap under the weight of a ladder, while the busy wasps made me wary of shinning up the trees.

Few of the imbecilic government slogans that the authorities delighted in sending farmers made much sense, but we agreed with the one advising that corn ricks should be made small and spaced well apart in case enemy air raids set them alight. Our corn stacks stood like circular tea cosies dotted along the farm track.

Dad always built our stacks, making them beautifully symmetrical. That day Jimmy Spit pitched from the load, tossing the sheaves across to me, while I in turn pitched them from the stack edge across to Dad. This was fine all the time the stack was not up to roof level, but once it was as high as Jimmy could comfortably reach with a six foot pitchfork, I took up station on the sloping roof side, where a few sheaves missed out from a couple of layers provided a precarious ledge just large enough for a pair of feet and a sheaf of corn, this being in farming parlance the 'lubber's hole'. To work in this was sheer hard labour, but infinitely safer than changing places with tobacco chewing Jimmy on the load.

By the time we were topping out the roof of the stack, both Dad and Spitting Jimmy were vaguely apologetic for being grumpy, making the excuse that everyone was getting edgy since the Nazi doodle-bugs began buzzing about. We had cheered when the first flying bombs passed overhead earlier that summer, believing that their jet flame meant they had all been set on fire by some marvellous secret weapon.

We soon learned differently, and by the time we were gathering the wheat harvest a line of heavy anti-aircraft guns was positioned across our quiet countryside, the object being to bring down the V1's in the areas of low population or deflect their course and turn them back out to sea.

We finished one wheat stack about midday and went over to the rowan tree to eat our food in its shade. We sat munching, with Jimmy contemplating a good swig from the stone bottle and cursing wasps, horse-flies and every other kind of flying bug, with good cause.

As the guns two fields away began to fire we heard a V1's engine cut out. Heads down, we counted to seven, then experienced a weird sensation as if we were caught in a loud surging current, breathlessly struggling in the surf of an invisible sea.

When the shock wave subsided we took stock of the situation. Jimmy was sure that the doodle-bug had been specifically sent by Hitler to spoil his harvest beer. It had solved the problem of picking the wild fruit: damsons, codlins and bullaces lay like a carpet on the stubbled field. The stack we had just finished had a definite list to port and the gate post I had knocked earlier in the morning now lay horizontal in the field.

"I reckon we ought to charge the government for fixing that, come the slack time this winter," said my father.

"I'd let that bloody post bide where it be, mate," Jimmy said, pausing from cutting chunks off an onion to eat with his bread and cheese ration. "There be too many mad tractor drivers and other awkward cusses about."

The Hop Picking Lark

Transcending all the familiar sounds of the waking city, young Barney Shilling heard his mother's early morning voice hoarse and rasping. She called him to get up. He had long learned the wisdom of keeping on the right side of her temper on mornings after both parents had spent a convivial evening in the 'Capstan and Compass', then staggered home to fight like cat and dog.

Barney and his four younger brothers had spent the previous evening picking berries on a bombed site. Consequently little Billy, who shared the bottom half of the bed with Barney, had disturbed his brother's slumbers by being spectacularly sick. Volcanoes of rage would have erupted had Barney called his mother out of the pub to deal with the crisis, just as they would when she eventually found the revolting mess on the unsheeted mattress and blanket coverings.

Scrambling over Burt, Bruce and Bob, all feigning sleep at the top end of the bed, Barney's bare toes explored the inside of his sandshoes. He hauled up his threadbare shorts to meet the T-shirt he had slept in, then ran down the dark uncarpeted stairway, which always reeked of kippers and next-door's tom cat. His mother stood by the ash-heaped kitchen hearth, rolling the bleached ends of her hair into curlers, coughing spasmodically as she lifted her arms above her head. Barney watched her haggard reflection in the fly-spotted mirror.

"Don't stand there gawping, unless you want a touch of your father's belt behind you. He's left me without so much as a fagend, so nip along to Ma Slavinsky and say you want five Woodbine on the book."

Sorting among the clutter on the sideboard Barney found the little red sixpenny note-book that served as an unofficial passport, giving the Shilling family access to the goods in Mrs. Slavinsky's corner shop.

The complete antithesis to his mother, Mrs. Slavinsky was enormous, every bulge and spare tyre of fat quivering whenever she moved or laughed. Few of her smiles were aimed in the Shillings' direction, although she was always kind to Barney, offering him titbits of dried raisins or broken liquorice bootlaces when there were no other customers about. On the credit sale of five Woodbines she was adamant. "My life. Are Hymie Rothschild and Abe Rockerfeller my cousins by marriage, ask your mother? Do I lay awake at night worrying how much you Shillings owe me already? Am I finding a gold mine shaft beneath my cellar that I can watch my capital go up in your mother's Woodbine smoke. Tell her there'll be no fags, no tick and no welcome in my shop until she pays off what she owes."

Daunted by the prospect of returning home empty handed, Barney hesitated. The old shopkeeper gave him a stale cake and a Shalom. Still stalling for time, Barney dragged his feet along the gutter, then sat down on the edge of the pavement to share his cake with Widow Mutton's mongrel dog.

The miserable little back street was not yet wide awake behind its drab, dusty curtains; the paving stones were wet with morning dew. At the street end, down toward the river, the dockyard cranes, the factory chimneys and the gas-holder at the reeking gas works were all shrouded in sulphurous, phlegm-foul fog, yet above his head was a patch of blue sky, and the first glimpse of watery September sunshine.

Perched high on the cowl of Widow Mutton's front room chimney, a speckled brown bird began to sing. Suddenly Barney experienced a great upsurge of his spirits that could only be expressed by bursting into song. Down the street the postman was delivering buff envelopes to first one house then another. Here was Barney's shield from his mother's anger. He ran home to tell her: "Mum, Mum the hop picking letters have come. I saw Mrs. Jenkins run across to Widow Mutton. They've both got theirs."

"Where's ours, then?" his mother retorted, following him back out into the street. Barney ran after the postman and asked if the Shilling's letter had been overlooked.

"Shilling," said the postman, as if the name rang bells in his memory. "Isn't Shilling the name where any bill or invoice we deliver gets sent back to the sorting office, 'Address unknown'? You're the kid that was singing in the street back there, aren't you? Tell your mother that I'll see if there is any mail lying around before the midday delivery starts, and say I told you that if she's hard up she ought to put you to singing in the halls."

Morning in the Shilling household passed by in a succession of tea-drinking neighbours offering commiserations that the Shilling's four-week holiday in the country seemed so uncertain, when their own arrangements were all signed and sealed. One or two hinted that the hop grower might have seen more than enough of the five Shilling boys. It was not only because they shared the same initial that made some folk refer to them as those five little B's.

Too unsettled to play on the bomb sites when neighbouring hop-garden bound children were helping collect and paint identification marks on every old tin bath, basket or substantial box they could muster, Barney, Bruce, Burt, Bob and the still queasy-stomached Billy punched a few heads, then formed a deputation to meet the postman on his rounds.

It was there. Notification that Mrs. Shilling and family had been allocated sleeping accommodation at King's Court Farm. Pickers to arrive not later than 11 a.m. on Saturday. Tally basket numbering and hop picking to begin on Monday at seven sharp.

Transport to the hop gardens was to be provided by the

coalman driving his big new lorry, him being Widow Mutton's nephew and doing the thirty mile journey cheap. Widow Mutton was regarded as being somewhat aristocratic, having a regular order of a half-pint bottle of cow's milk every morning from the milkman, while any milk the Shilling family used came from tins. She was definitely someone to be cultivated at hop picking time because she took along a spirit stove, and while Mrs. Shilling needed to coax a kindling wood open fire to boil a kettle of water, Widow Mutton had the means of making a quick cup of tea.

Barney and Bert were sent to collect all the goods and chattels that their grandmother would be taking to the hop picking, wheeling it to their home on a soap box cart. Gran lived half-a-mile away so they did not see her very often.

She was tiny, her frame twisted with arthritis, her hands like chicken claws, her nose and chin almost meeting when she dispensed with wearing her false teeth. Tap-tapping along, shouting and waving her walking stick in her effort to restrain her high spirited grandsons, she was quite exhausted by the time they were passing the Capstan And Compass, so she popped in for a rest and to get a 'little something' for their mum.

Mrs. Slavinsky was someone else Barney was sent to deal with. He took two pound notes and a message from his mother to the effect that the backlog of debt would be reduced, if not cleared, by the Shilling's hop picking money. Barney cajoled the old shopkeeper into giving credit for some groceries and five assorted pairs of the special line she was offering in cheap and substantial Wellington boots.

Even with boxes, baskets, baths and backless chairs piled up over the cab of the lorry, Barney was sure there would never be room for all the goods and people trying to cram together on almost new coal sacks spread across the back. Nevertheless, with Billy on his lap, squeezed in with the other children leaning against the tailgate, Barney watched the scenery change as the lorry climbed up and out of the city.

With the sun on his face and the air rushing past he felt that same indefinable uplift of spirit that always forced him to lift his head and sing.

"Voice of an angel, your Barney," said the woman whose

elbows were prodding Barney's mother. "Little devil, more likely," Mrs. Shilling replied, dismissing her son's gift.

They arrived at the hopper's huts in a welter of lost baggage, wet-bottomed children and excitement, finding their allotted number in the rows of wooden hutments, each with less living space than most right-minded country cottagers would have deemed adequate to house a couple of fattening backyard pigs.

Puzzled by the noisy invasion, farm horses stamped their enormous hooves and nervously pricked their ears as they stood in the shafts of waggons loaded with wood faggots for cooking fires and oat straw and oat chaff 'flights' to fill makeshift mattresses. Some pickers managed to instil a semblance of homeliness in their huts, but Mrs. Shilling had no such houseproud inclinations. Despite this, Barney knew that by sandwiching themselves between a couple of 'chaffies', huge clean hop-pocket sacks filled with oat flights, they slept warmer, cleaner, and in greater comfort within the confines of their hopping hut than in the bed all five boys shared at home.

In a cluster of tents, the hop gardens mission workers brewed field coppers of tea as a Christian gesture of welcome. After dark they built a huge camp fire, encouraging the pickers to gather around for a friendly singsong. Nicknamed 'Holy Joe' by the irreverent pickers, the young missioner in charge of the proceedings called out, "Is there anyone here who can sing?" Barney found himself being pushed forward toward the fire. His heart and his voice rose with the sparks ascending skyward. The circle of pickers fell silent, listening to an urchin singing like a lark.

Ragged, thin and all too conscious of the shortcomings of his background, any childhood illusions Barney might have once cherished had long since been nullified by an indolent mother's disinterest and a pub-crawling father's leather belt. He knew happiness as an infrequent will-o-the-wisp sensation, but for those few glorious weeks of September magic in Kings Court Farm hop gardens, his sheer exhilaration induced the familiar compulsive feeling that he must either sing or burst.

Encouraged by 'Holy Joe', Barney sang solo after solo. Unaware of the impact he was having on what was his first real audience, he stood by the camp fire, warm, watching a round September moon rising, pouring out the elation of his heart. Except for the clear young voice there was absolute stillness until a brushwood faggot, placed on the fire's depleted embers, sent a volcano of sparks erupting into the night sky, then settled into a flaring flame that somehow broke the spell of Barney's voice.

A murmur of approval surged into spontaneous clapping, then Barney heard the chink of coins being thrown around his feet. As he stooped to collect his unexpected bonus his face turned crimson with family shame.

"He's the eldest of the Shilling tribe," a woman close to him was explaining to her neighbour. "How the poor little devil can sing like a bird when he gets more back-handers and bashings than breakfasts is beyond me. I'd be ashamed for my kid to stand there with legs like broomsticks and no backside to his breeches. Don't chuck your money to him, love. He won't see none of it, and I for one am not buying beer to pour down that Shilling woman's neck, or her old mother's."

Sick with humiliation, Barney tried to creep away from the circle of the fire, but Holy Joe saw him. Hot baked potatoes were to be passed around and in Holy Joe's estimation, Barney had earned his share.

As Barney's mother took his collection of coppers his Gran, chumbling on a baked potato, suddenly became aware of a personal crisis. "Oh, my gawd," she cackled, "I've gone and left me teeth at home." His mother's reference to the wizened old woman as a "daft old faggot," contributed nothing to family harmony. Gran countered with the ultimatum that she would neither pick hops nor set foot in The Fox And Duck down in the village minus her false teeth. Mrs. Shilling seemed to regard both contingencies as catastrophic. Listening to the arguing women, Holy Joe asked how long a journey of recovery might take.

Too dim-witted to appreciate the distance a fast lorry can cover in 90 minutes, Barney's mother estimated it would take a young man like himself some three hours walk. "No problem then," said Holy Joe, trying to be helpful. "Barney can borrow the mission bike and slip back for the dentures tomorrow morning.

"In return I would like him to sing a solo at the Festival of Harvest Thanksgiving we are sharing with all denominations of the local people in the village church tomorrow night."

"You hear that, Barney?" said his mother. "Just you mind that you do what 'the reverent' says."

Barney had no time to speculate on the deficiencies of the mission bike when he left on the following morning. Oil starved, rattling, cursed with a wobbling saddle, it was too high for Barney to ride in safety or comfort. Marco Polo, orientating eastward, could have endured no more qualms than Barney venturing in unknown country.

Putting his stamina in unequal contest with an uphill climb by standing on the pedals, he felt his knees give way beneath him and fell off into the hedge. As he paused to rest he heard a vehicle climbing the hill behind him. A blue van passed, then stopped. A police sergeant and a constable got out. Barney's immediate action was one of utter amazement that the narrow lane should merit police attention. With miles of nothing but empty corn fields, what could anyone steal?

"That your bike, son?" The sergeant was not unfriendly. Barney only wished he could claim the social status of being a bike owner, but explained about the mission worker and his grandmother's teeth. "Where would they be then?" the sergeant asked.

"With the knives and forks in her kitchen drawer," Barney answered, wondering why both policemen laughed. Looking around the bike they said that only mission prayers could account for the fact that the wheels were still turning. It needed a spanner and an oil can around it. They gave Barney a lift to the main police station in the city, put his bike right and sent him on his way.

With the saddle fixed and lowered he found it easier to keep the wheels turning once he had left the 'cop-shop'. It took only a few minutes to reach his grandmother's terraced home and collect the set of stained and yellowing teeth. His way back took him past his own home, but being Sunday morning he knew that his father and his hangover were always best left undisturbed.

Mrs. Slavinsky, outside her corner general shop that sold everything from arrowroot to second-hand coal shovels, waved to him, calling. "You became so rich with hop-picking that you're back, riding a bike already?"

Having explained his mission Barney said he had to hurry

back because Holy Joe wanted him to sing for a lot of country people at a church festival that night.

"This is a rabbi person, and he lets you ride sixty miles on that thing? So he heard you sing then. And does he find you some different clothes before you stand up singing to these fine people? Of course not. Without money what can you do?" Barney told her about the money he had collected round the camp fire. It would have helped his situation.

"Barney one day your voice will earn you pounds, not pennies, so here's what I'll do. Strictly business. I'll find you an almost new shirt and a pair of trousers, a bit big perhaps, but your tail end won't be showing. Then when you get rich you can pay me back. Soft in the head I must be getting, but to send you on a sixty mile journey then ask you to sing a solo? That I should have been given such a son."

A flat tyre delayed Barney so much that he could hear the village church bells ringing before he reached the hop-picking encampment. His brother, Bob, told him that Holy Joe had left him the message to get to the church as fast as he could.

His mother thought him clever to have got anything from Ma Slavinsky without cash or account book and, as a reward for getting Gran's teeth back, allowed him to dip both pieces of his bread and margarine into the sugar bag. Barney gobbled them down, anxious to get away.

"Gran, me and the kids are taking a stroll down the village, and I ain't having you get so high and mighty with this singing in church stunt that you can't walk down with us."

Mrs. Shilling suppressed his protests with the back of her hand. Bent almost double, Gran's pace of walking was snail-like. By the time they reached the village the churchgoers were leaving, and Barney realised that he was too late. The evening was suddenly cold.

"Never mind, Barney." His mother's voice was wheedling in tone, far different than usual. "You wouldn't have got any tips there, but if you give us a song or two outside the pub door I might find enough from what people give to buy you kids some crisps."

As if in response to Barney's utter desolation Holy Joe came striding up behind them. If he had overheard Mrs. Shilling's suggestion he gave no sign.

"Sorry you got back too late, Barney. I am sure you boys would not want to spoil the last chance of a bit of recreation your good mother and grandmother will have before picking starts tomorrow. Don't worry about them Mrs. Shilling. I will see them safely back to camp."

Tucked snugly between his chaffies Barney reviewed the day that was almost over. He had seen more of the countryside than he imagined to have existed. He had gained a new shirt and some trousers and had ridden in a police van. True he had missed singing at the festival, but Holy Joe seemed to understand the situation. Tomorrow hop picking would begin. A whole month of September magic stretched before him.

One day, when his singing made him rich, he would buy a house near the hop gardens, ordering groceries by the ton from Ma Slavinsky, strictly for cash.

The Sunday Paperman

The only way daily newspapers were delivered in the village was by getting the wholesale newsagent in the city to send them out by post. At a penny for the paper plus a halfpenny postage, this seemed expensive, many regarding it as absolute extravagance to spend money on reading about a lot of old 'furriners fighting' or 'them politicals talking out the back side of their heads', when the postman, scanning through the headlines in his post bag, would willingly impart the gist of yesterday's stale news. Giving the lie to their implied thriftlessness, those who indulged in buying daily papers made sure that no scraps went to waste.

Apart from being folded, cut into small squares and threaded on a string to hang on a nail in the 'out back', it served in various other ways. Apples, wrapped in newspaper and stored in cupboards or under the back room bed, kept firm until well past Christmas. Soaked to a pulp and sealing up draughty skirting boards or ill fitting windows, paper kept the winter winds at bay. Many a ploughman plodding the wintery furrows found comfort from a newspaper tucked under his jersey to keep his chest warm, with another couple of sheets keeping his kidneys cosy at the back.

Local weeklies came via the market day bus and the Post Office counter, but thanks to a lukewarm but longstanding romance between the saddler's daughter and a bald bachelor newsagent who had a small shop in the city, we collected a Sunday newspaper without fail. He always parked his motorcycle and boxed sidecar in the saddler's backyard shed. Spurred on by cups of cocoa, the newsagent spent too much time trying to persuade his prospective wife and future mother-in-law that a maiden of thirty five is not too young to marry.

Knowing that his regular customers were relatively honest, he trusted them to serve themselves and put the correct money in the enamel basin left on the motorbike seat.

Collecting the Sunday paper gave a cast iron excuse for the men who awaited high noon when the Hare and Hounds opened. Lady customers could exchange details of the latest village news while their Sunday dinner cooked. It made for friendliness and harmless gossip, but when I rode down for the paper one Michaelmas Sunday morning, I found that this atmosphere had entirely disappeared.

The village policeman was there with his pencil and notebook at the ready, asking if I could remember if anyone was in the shed when I had collected the paper on the previous Sunday, or if I had seen any strangers on my way home.

Glum faced at having to miss his cocoa and comfort, the bald newsagent said that in all the eighteen years he had courted the saddler's daughter, he had never been more than a couple of pence short in his newspaper money and never a foreign coin given as change. Now, when some light fingered sneak thief had pinched both money and basin, he was rapidly coming to the conclusion that it was not worth trailing out to the village for a measly cup of cocoa, and was seriously considering calling off his lacklustre love affair and his paper round.

The parson's sister and I had collected our papers at the same time the previous Sunday, and for once I welcomed her company, for the new under gamekeeper from The Hall was close behind. I had never felt the slightest apprehension about living and working in the depths of the country, but on several occasions during the few months he had been in the district, I had been aware of him watching behind bushes or standing around on the edge of Church Woods as I worked in the fields.

His swaggering attitude annoyed me so I gave him no encouragement realising that he had roving eyes and hands to match. He had followed me into the saddler's yard on the previous Sunday, but any suggestion that he might be the culprit was dismissed by our guardian of the law. The underkeeper had come to the Hall with excellent references from some of the highest aristocracy in the land. Only that week he had earned His Lordship's approbation in catching an estate hand trying to hide poached game.

I didn't care if the angels sang his praises, or if he had captured a gang of poachers single handed, every instinct warned me that he was trouble come amongst folk of honesty and mutual trust.

As I started back home, Slippy Springer the village poacher, chimney sweep and grave digger, came pedalling along on his rattling old bike, then rode along beside me, saying he wanted a quiet word with my Dad. Naturally our conversation centred on the stolen paper money and my suspicions. Slippy said quietly, "You're right to worry about that fly-by-night underkeeper. Just you be careful, Jo."

If Slippy came onto our land it was usually without our knowledge or permission, so Mum and Dad were intrigued to see him standing at the back door that Sunday morning and promptly asked him in.

"'Tis like this, Harry!" he began. "I don't need to tell you that this underkeeper bloke is a sly one. I've been telling your Jo that I've seen him standing prying and peering at her. She may be skinny as a bean pole stood up sideways, but he be after anything in skirts."

What little vanity I had evaporated with Slippy's evaluation of my beauty, but Mum thanked him for the warning.

"Well, missus!" Slippy answered. "That's not why I came! I've come up here to ask Harry's advice and borrow a tarpaulin stack cover. One of the estate hands is being evicted first thing on Michaelmas morning because he caught that slimy devil trying to maul his missus and gave him a fair old tousling before chucking him in the pond. Next thing he knew was that all three gamekeepers were in his cottage garden and peering down the well. They hauled up six brace of pheasants with rabbit snares round their necks."

Dad remarked that the estate worker might have been trying to make a bit of extra money by selling the birds to posh hotels which preferred game that was not peppered with shot.

"What!" Slippy grunted. "With the homemade snares the old keeper that left took off me last winter? That cunning snipe cut holes in the wire netting you set around Stony Field, and if he had been a few minutes later the other morning, I would have gained twelve pheasants and got my own rabbit snares back. Instead he used them to get revenge on that young couple. It troubles me badly, but I daren't shout the odds about it, because if I admitted I was trespassing in search of game I could be 'His Majesty's guest' for another twenty eight days. If you could drop a word in the right direction it might help them youngsters, or if they are evicted lend them the use of a waterproof cover to protect their furniture, for the only place they'll have for it is alongside the road."

Dad took a Sunday evening stroll through the woods to see the head gamekeeper, who promised to re-check his underling's credentials.

The underkeeper got wind of what was happening and by the next weekend he was gone. So was the saddler's daughter, taking her father's life savings with her.

The Sunday paperman drove off out of the saddler's yard in a roar of anger and exhaust fumes, and we villagers had to accept the fact that if we wanted to read the Sunday apers, we would have to wait for the following Tuesday morning's post.

Not Quite Cricket

This is the first home match of the cricket season. The white attired Lockley team, our traditional opponents, saunter around in nonchalant groups as if they are rehearsing a television commercial for a new detergent giving a whiter brighter wash. Making loud disparaging remarks about the condition of our sloping pitch, they calculate the probable tonnage per acre if the grass on outfield is ever mown for hay. This is sheer sarcasm designed to undermine the finer feelings of Popper Button and his band of stalwarts who have spent all morning driving Hugh's Friesian herd to temporary pastures, and clearing up the pitch.

Affectionately known as 'The Shovel and Pancake Brigade' to all our club supporters, the good hearted old volunteers have laboured hard and long.

Time was when the young men of the village would willingly

have forgone beer, skittles, overtime or courting, hoping that their presence at Tuesday and Thursday evening practice sessions behind Chappell's cowsheds, might persuade Popper Button, then the captain, to select them for our team to oppose Lockley in the yearly match.

It was then a matter of village pride, almost a bounden duty, that every able bodied person in the parish should go to cheer on Popper and his gallant cricket team. It is just another indication of declining standards to admit that today our team seems underpowered, scratched together with the help of an arthritic-inclined grandfather acting wicketkeeper, and two surprised but enthusiastic thirteen year old lads.

Despite all this, none of our club members seems despondent. We all share the secret that our newest member is so fast and furious a bowler that he runs the risk of launching himself into powered flight whenever he sends a sharp delivery up the pitch. Granted, he is a physical training college type given to jogging around the village each morning long before the ground is aired. Lockley-ites stare in disbelief to see him limbering up by sprinting round the pitch in a luminous yellow track suit.

In their day, Popper and his old stagers were content to defend the cricket honour of the village, fortified by belt and braces to support their corduroy trousers as they hurled down 'chinamen', 'bumpers' and 'yorkers', but this we overlook because the new man lives just over Lockley parish boundary and could well have been their secret weapon instead of ours.

This being so, he and his wife receive constant reassurance of the neighbourliness of our community by way of the odd sack of spuds, eggs, and occasional cabbage, when comparable supplies in Lockley shops are either dear or scarce.

Suspicious that we have once again resorted to some devious subterfuge he has not yet fathomed, the Lockley captain complains that fresh cow pats on the wicket were deliberately left there as a hazard to his players. For his part, no play will start until they are cleared. Popper trots across the pitch, shovel at the ready, marvelling aloud that Hugh's heifers would invade the batting area when there has been a single strand wire fence around it for the last week, and this with a clearly printed notice warning, 'Keep Off'.

Our captain makes the logical observation that our players

run as much risk of injury as any Lockley-ite, but the opposition seem to think that although Popper is a first-rate ambulance man at any other time of crisis, his cricketing loyalties might let him leave any injured Lockley player lying until stumps are drawn.

Lockley has experienced the same difficulties in finding enough players to field a full team as we have, so no one takes much notice of the shy willow-slim young stranger introduced as their eleventh man, hurriedly enlisted to make their number up.

Some misguided souls have fondly imagined this young player to be Lockley score-keeper's daughter, and as our captain walks over to win the toss with Hugh's double headed penny, he is heard to express the view that with Lockley being forced to field girlish characters with blow-waved blonde hair against our new demon bowler, the game should be a pushover. Determined to demoralize them from the start, he sends Lockley in to bat.

There is no nonsense about using the shine of a new ball for a fast bowler. Any shine disappeared while it stayed in the box after last season's matches. Nevertheless our new acquisition tears into Lockley batting until they are six down for twenty-four in the sixteenth over. Popper Button and the rest of his old cronies, sitting on the bench in front of our converted chicken house pavilion, express approval and the confident hope that it will all be over, bar the shouting before tea.

Popper's wife, Pearl, hearing this prediction, lights the flame under the tea urn. She had been a bit 'poorly-like' since her recent intricate and highly personal abdominal operation, so she calls for assistance from the watchers outside to help lift a plastic can of water to top up the tea urn.

At this instant our bowler, hurtling along his run up, slips and falls heavily on his shoulder just as he is raising his arm to bowl. The air seems to quiver with his screaming, then he passes out cold. His yells have the same effect on Popper and Pearl as distress flares to a lifeboat. They both scurry across the pitch to offer first aid. They make a cursory examination of our fallen idol who starts whimpering in an unmanly fashion.

"What do you reckon to it, Popper?" Pearl asks kneeling to place a tea towel under the young man's head because it is perilously close to a rather wet cow pat. This sets him yelling once again. "Obvious, old love!" says Popper. "Dislocation!" they remark in unison. It is pointless to ask if there is a doctor on the field.

Making reassuring noises, Popper tells our toppled hero that they will get a car across and take him to the casualty department of the city hospital. "Don't try to move me!" bawls the stricken athlete. Popper dispatches someone to fetch the first aid kit he never fails to bring on such occasions. He administers a quick slurp from the water bottle. Unappreciatively, the injured man complains that it tastes of warm rust, then faints again.

"Right!" says Popper authoritatively, realising that this gives him an opportunity to do the manipulative therapy he deems urgent and essential. Enlisting the help of the gawping players clustered round him, he tells them to hold the bowler down, and keep him perfectly still. Pearl, meanwhile, is clasping the patient round his neck as if she intends to pull his head off. Digging in his heels, Popper quickly grasps the arm attached to the injured shoulder, hauls on it as if he were practising to be the anchor man in a tug-of-war-team, then yanks it upwards. There is a sudden popping sound, like a cork coming out of a champagne bottle. It can be heard above the patient's curses and groans. Suddenly he sits up looking white and sheepish as Popper explains how the ball joint he had jolted out of its socket has been put into place again. He staggers into the pavilion to be given a cup of strong sweet tea. Pearl's sovereign remedy for shock.

The cricket fanatics who have lost interest in his welfare since he can no longer set Lockley wickets tumbling, are more concerned that we are fielding one man short in this needle game.

The rest is left to our more mundane bowlers and two leg before wicket decisions given by an umpire, not so much biased as having a due regard for his native village. With a hint of rain in the air and Lockley all out for forty in ninety minutes, the captains agree to continue with another hour of play before taking tea.

With his score nought, not out, having had no chance to face the bowling at the end of their innings, Lockley's effeminate looking eleventh man has done nothing to alter our team's opinion that he is a bit of a giggle. It comes as a surprise to our two opening batsmen to see Lockley team moving around to his instructions as he places his fielders in readiness to bowl. He tucks his long blonde tresses beneath a multicoloured headband, then proceeds to hurl down short pitched, high spinning fast deliveries that force our batsmen to play strokes more agricultural than authentic, or duck out of the way.

Molehills, sheep sent to stray across the pitch, a collie trained to catch and retrieve on the boundary, plus a few other minor diversions have all been recognised as legitimate strategems in our annual battle with Lockley, but Popper Button is not alone in his assertion that there has been nothing to match this in the last fifty years.

Popper's first reaction as the long haired bowler leaps down the pitch like a kangaroo with blisters, is that Lockley has imported one of them Australian fellows, but fair play to Australia, their breed of fast bowlers never pretend to be shy, simpering, long haired lilies who couldn't tell a leg-bye from a thigh pad. Only Lockley could dream up an underhand stunt like that.

It is misery to watch, and suffice it to say that we consider our team lucky to have made double figures by tea time. Tom Grommett's nose has almost stopped bleeding, and everyone applauds the bravery of a man who, rather than flinch in the face of danger, takes off his bi-focal glasses so as not to see it. Modest as ever, he admits that National Health or not, those glasses cost him a fair packet, so he doesn't dare to break them. All he could do was to close his eyes when he heard the ball whistling down the pitch, and hang out his bat to dry.

As tea and cucumber sandwiches are dispensed in the pavilion, Popper quietly agrees with our captain that we are on a good hiding to nothing. All that can be done now is to drag out the tea break to give our injured bowler as long as possible to recover from the pain in his right shoulder, then hope he can keep his end up as last man in.

Our captain issues his instructions. "Pass the word round. Give Lockley all the tea and cakes they can stuff, and keep them talking."

Popper ploughs straight in, asking the Lockley wicketkeeper if his mother's brother-in-law by her second marriage wasn't the driver of his ambulance back in his days in voluntary first aid. There is some discussion among the teams until this fact is established, village rivalry being momentarily suspended because both parishes shared the old subscription ambulance, making it permissable and even honourable for brigade members from either parish to work side by side.

"Where did you learn to put dislocated joints back into place then?" The Lockley captain asks Popper. Some heathen from the far side of Lockley boundary comments on the fact that Popper worked in a slaughterhouse before he retired, but his insinuating remarks are ignored. We know that when Popper Button starts talking about voluntary first aid work, it is like making a small hole in dam wall, and a torrent of anecdotes can easily be unleashed.

Popper reminisces about the days when Pearl and he were courting and saving so hard to get married, they had no money to spare on going out. Joining the ambulance corps presented them with the opportunity to gain free admission to shows and important happenings for miles around.

In the days of the silent movies, it was feared that such dramatic realism might cause patrons to faint, so volunteer first aiders were on duty for every performance. Pearl interjects that there has been nothing to match those old 'fillums' at the Electric Picture Theatre ever since. Minutes pass, Pearl and her helpers taking their time to top up tea cups as Popper repeats his oft-told story of the night Old Henery from the pig farm fell from a loft to land head first in his old sow's farrowing pen. Mid-winter, knee-deep in mire, Popper and the ambulance driver from Lockley trudged along the rutted track with their stretcher to find their patient still lying in the muck, unconscious or dead drunk. Old Henery was heavy and took a lot of lifting. Plodding back through mud as thick as lumpy custard, Popper confessed that he was so near exhaustion, he feared he would drop his end of the stretcher before they reached the ambulance out on the hard road. Old Henery sat up cursing. "If you're going to rock the boat, mate, I'll carry your end of this contraption to the end of the track."

This he did, only climbing back onto the stretcher to be lifted into the ambulance, then they set off, covered in pig muck, all warning bells a-ringing. Popper's wry sense of humour as he spins his yarn inspires amusement in our injured player, reminding the Lockley-ites why they are here.

The Lockley captain sarcastically enquires if the fact that our lot are sitting around the pavilion like a consignment of mutton in a butchery cold store means that we concede defeat to a better team. If not, it is high time we got back on the pitch to take a thrashing. A sporadic patter of apprehensive clapping offers condolence to our batting pair returning to the fray.

Last man in, and leaving the pavilion with as much enthusiasm as a turkey feels for Christmas, our demon bowler bats left handed facing theirs. Suddenly there is a spot of rain. Then another. And another. Soon the pitch is waterlogged and we all gather in the pavilion, steaming around the tea urn. Both sides have tried their tricks and dishonour is satisfied.

Smudge

Red eyed with hatred for her owner, the wretched collie bitch defied his attempts to approach the draughty barrel to which she was chained. Wielding a long handled rake, he had hauled out and destroyed all but one of her newborn litter, so the abject creature guarded her surviving pup with desperate, bare-fanged fury, lavishing on it an affection she had never encountered during the years that she had been a chained prisoner guarding the gateway to a few old sheds and the scrap metal dump where her disreputable owner plied a dubious trade.

I first saw the fat little female pup when she was about a fortnight old and no longer sightless waddling around on unsteady legs to explore the world beyond the crumbling kennel. Floundering in mud made viscid by her mother's dragging chain, the pup lay whimpering until the collie patiently took her back into the barrel and lovingly licked her clean. Seeing me watching from the gate, the scrap metal dealer explained that he wanted to get the pup away because feeding their young made watchdogs lazy. His reactions to my outspoken comment on the old collie's lamentably thin condition was the observation that a bit of healthy hunger helped to keep a dog fit and alert.

I knew that any quixotic ideas about setting the old dog free would end disastrously for some farmer's sheep flock, so I saved scraps of our own poultry and pig food, and threw them to the hungry bitch whenever I went past. It came to the point where I felt guilty if I missed cycling over to the scrap yard, and the collie recognised the rattle of my old bike. The furious barking that warned off strangers, diminished to yaps and her mud-caked drooping tail responded as I approached the gate. Still wary for her infant's safety, she administered a sharp nip and a shove back into the kennel if the pup ventured out. As the pup grew rounder, her mother became more skeletal. If a totting expedition coincided with a drinking session, the dealer sometimes stayed away from the scrap yard for days, but I tried my best to see that the old dog had water and was fed.

The collie kept her baby safe for a month or so, but then one morning I heard a terrible commotion as I approached the scrap yard gate. Infuriated snarls rasped from the bitch's throat as it fought against the restraining collar. I saw the dealer standing between the straying pup and her mother with an axe shaft in his hand. As he saw me and told me to go away in extremely basic language, his hesitation gave the pup an opportunity to scuttle behind a pile of scrap metal, whimpering all the while.

The dealer cornered her in an old oil drum but space proved too restricted for him to wield his axe shaft. As he grabbed the small squirming animal and headed towards a shed, I went with him, threatening to get the police to make an unwelcome visit to his yard, and in return he promised me prosecution for trespass, plus the axeshaft round my head. Knowing that the pup would be slaughtered immediately I left, I offered to take it away. The dealer's attitude altered. He asked if I imagined he was daft enough to destroy a valuable puppy, explaining that he intended to start its sheepdog training early. Seeing that I had shown so much interest and appreciation of the fine points of a pure bred collie, he offered it for sale at the 'ridiculously' low price of one pound.

I was saving for some new winter shoes, but the sight of the axe shaft in his hairy hand made me accept his offer. It was only when I was safely outside the gate with the cowering little pup tucked under my coat that I realised that in passing I had stopped to stroke the old collie's head. She had not growled or snapped at me, but sat disconsolately on her haunches, watching me take away her pup with huge brown mournful eyes. Her misery haunted me, so later in the day, I rode back to feed her, but the barrel was empty, and her long rusting chain with the broken old collar lay in the mud. The dealer had by that time gone to the Cottage Hospital to get treatment for dog bites on his face and arms.

Taking the pup home was an exercise in diplomacy. Dad had always maintained that geese and peafowl gave better warning of strangers than any canine. The added advantage that they laid eggs and provided festive meals, meant that there were no dogs on our farm.

"You've bought what?" Mum raised her hands in horror, scattering a shower of flour from the pastry bowl into her hair. "You need a dog like I need toothache!" she grumbled. "I'll bet it is heaving with worms and fleas!"

Unmindful of these remarks, the pup found the unaccustomed luxury of the warm hearthrug, scratched itself lethargically, then went to sleep.

'Elgar' seemed a suitable name for the pup because the variations of her breed were a complete enigma, but when Dad saw her asleep on the hearthrug, he said she looked more like a smudge of dirty boot marks on the mat than twenty shillings worth of dog. In fact, he said, he would make it his business to see the dealer and demand nineteen and sixpence back.

It is hard to describe Smudge's shape or colour, for she resembled a frayed fluffy tangle of old grey and black mixtured sock wool as a puppy, developing a curly coated spaniel build, long floppy ears, and a miniscule tail like a short length of chewed string.

Mum still complained that a dog could be a nuisance as I explained the background story, but she gave Smudge a saucer of warm milk and suggested that she mix up some wormballs. These worm eradicating pellets of dough, laced with fennel and wild garlic, seemed a dubious kind of welcome, but I knew from that moment that Smudge was safely home.

As a house-dog she was useless, greeting strangers with the same enthusiasm that she offered guests. Farm cats and fowls completely over-awed her, and she tried to give the rooster a wide berth. She became my shadow from dawn until it was time for me to rack up the horses' mangers with hay in the evening, then she climbed an almost vertical ladder to sleep in the warmth of the stable loft. When I went ploughing with seagulls wheeling in a white winged cloud around me, Smudge plodded behind the rear wheel of the tractor, making friendly overtures to the screaming birds.

Rooks were a different proposition, a word to set her muzzle quivering with indignation, while an instruction to "See those rooks off then Smudge," transformed her into a supercharged mongrel racing over the ploughed furrows at such a pace that her mud-tipped long ears flapped up and down as if she might become airborne. She was often hampered by her short little forelegs treading on her ear tips, making her turn somersaults, but this never deterred her from scaring rooks, crows and jackdaws from the fields.

We made no attempt to train Smudge to work with sheep or cattle, but her intelligence saved miles of walking. If I suggested that she fetched a few straying ewes back, her chewed string rudder wiggled, and her ears bounced as she went eagerly about her task. She hated thunder and, during wartime air raids that were a fact of life in our corner of the country, some canine instinct warned her when we were in for a noisy time. Instead of trotting along behind the tractor, she ran ahead yapping, as if to say, "Do you want it in writing that there will be a raid?" If I ignored her, she soon set off home, only stopping when she was safely under Dad's old leather armchair. When she deemed it safe, she would appear again, greeting us effusively, all tongue and wiggling tail, as if to register her pleasure that such uncomprehending idiots had managed to survive.

Our 'farm-dog' was a standing joke among our friends and neighbours until a night just before one Christmas when Dad and I went out into the blackout to feed the horses and take Smudge to her stable loft. Some sound or movement attracted her attention and she crouched, whimpering, by my side. Carrying the dimmed lantern, Dad went toward the stable, but as I followed, I heard the rustle of boots on straw, then saw someone with a torch slip round the side of a rick to disappear into the shadows of the night.

Grabbing a pitchfork, I yelled to Dad, then ran in the direction of the fowl houses, Smudge staying close to my heels. Almost colliding with one intruder as I dodged round the straw rick. I prodded his behind with the business end of the pitchfork, but Smudge tore on ahead, displaying the same demented fury as her mother had shown on the day I bought her, snarling, barking by the chicken house door. Dad stood over the man I had floored, his lantern in one hand and a horse whip in the other. Amongst thumps, bumps, and a mêlée of squawking chickens, we heard our berserk dog and a screaming man imploring us to call the savage beast off. Smudge had never shown any sign of being savage before that night, nor did she again during the years of her short lifetime, and I have often wondered how she could have known that on the night two strangers came to steal our Christmas poultry, one of them had a loaded gun.

Room at the Inn

A single, smoke dried sprig of holly hanging above the dartboard acknowledged the Christmas season, but the bar of the Horse and Harrow was sparse comfort at any time of the year. The old fashioned 'spittoon and sawdust' country pub had wooden benches around walls darkened by tobacco smoke and brown paint, plus a few straight-backed chairs and beer stained tables on the bare quarry-tiled floor. The blackened oil lamp hanging from the ceiling cast a dim dispirited light that made the numbers on the dartboard in the far corner more a feat of memory than of observation. A sullen stove in a wide-hearthed fireplace emitted frequent billows of eye-smarting smoke, but gave out little heat.

Making desultory conversation with his first customer Jack Crookley, the shepherd, the landlord stood listening to the sound of singing coming from the village church and watching several adults and a horde of children hurrying up the church path.

"There's a fair old number turned out for tonight's rehearsal," the landlord remarked, "they tell me the only one who will take the part of Mary is Joe Gimble's missus."

"Good God," Jack exploded, "she sings sharp as lemons and wobbles her notes as if she's standing on a loose board."

When the old Christmas play was revived back in the nineteen thirties. Jack's own wife sang the part of Mary, sweet as a song thrush. It still made his eyes smart just thinking about her standing in blue and white crooning a lullaby to her own baby daughter asleep in the crib. Sometimes in the years that followed, a swaddling wrapped doll or a village baby was placed there, but never again could his wife play Mary, for when his daughter Ruth was less than a year old, the woman he adored fell from the top of a fruit-picking ladder and broke her back.

In the two years she lay bedridden before losing the battle for survival she was tended by friends and neighbourly women. These good hearted souls virtually adopted his daughter, making it possible for him to bring her up properly at home. Ruth had grown up with a strong resemblance to her mother, the way she walked, the way she laughed, the way she held her head.

She was clever too, passing exams and winning scholarships that took her away to college. For the last two years she had come home at the end of winter term to take the part of Mary in the village Christmas play. To hear Ruth singing to a doll in the nativity crib had made his soul weep, mumbling his lines as the first shepherd, thinking of his other Mary, and all the empty years.

Then last year in the tiny vestry of the church, with her blue and white robe still on her, his daughter had broken the news that she was expecting a child.

Sick with misery, disappointment, and a mixture of unfathomable feelings, Jack had voiced his strong beliefs and spoken harshly, ignoring Ruth's assertion that she and the child's father hoped to marry when their final exams were done. The upshot of this shattering incident was that Ruth caught the last bus out of the village on that Christmas Eve, leaving Jack to spend Christmas Day alone with the trappings of the holiday to mock him.

He knew it would not do to dwell now on the fact that no word had passed between them during the year, or that the letters he had written to her student lodgings had come back 'unknown'.

Jack had gone through the motions of living, this uncomfortable pub bar being the only companionable place for him to kill the empty hours after his working day was done.

Waiting for the landlady to take over behind the bar so that Tom, the landlord, and he could go to the play rehearsal together, Jack tried his hand at a practice round-the-clock game of darts. A remark of Tom's so distracted his concentration that the dart he was aiming at double top dislodged the holly above the board then flew back, flight downwards into his beer.

"Closing the pub on Christmas Day?" Jack could scarcely believe his ears. "I didn't think you publicans could shut up shop as if you were pork butchers or drapers, Tom! Are we regulars expected to spend all Christmas sitting at home and twiddling our thumbs?"

Tracing an intricate pattern in the spilt beer with one finger, Tom said, "Nothing in the licensing laws stops me having a quiet Christmas Day with my missus and friends if I want to. I'm supposed to offer sustenance, shelter and stabling to any bona fide traveller but if one should so happen to turn up this Christmas morning, he'll have to take pot luck with us.

"It's definite that this year I'm not propping up this ruddy bar waiting for regulars who always stay at home with their families on Christmas Day. Them that are so parched can get a bellyfull of flat beer and wind across at the Felled Ox."

"Where do I stand in your line of reckoning then Tom?" Jack asked.

"You!" Tom managed to get a plethora of meaning into that single word. "There are some that say you have more good friends and better kinfolk than you merit, even if you have had more than your fair share of misery in the past. I see Joe Gimble is coming across, he reckons he can't bear to hear his old woman screeching, so before he gets here, I can only say that if you can't face Christmas without young Ruth, then you must come and have dinner with us."

No more was said: Jack's eyes began to smart and water so he went across and prodded the smouldering fire with the toecap of his boot. It was all very well for Tom to talk of good friends but how could anyone convey the utter desolation of existing in a house that was a void of echoing silence?

Did Tom have the slightest inkling that every second, minute and hour of work or leisure was just time to kill in a world that for him had been shattered twice?

"Come on, my mule-headed old matey." Tom called him back to the realities of the present. "Let's get over to the church and say our piece."

The rehearsal was utter chaos, the mouse-like organist having lost her music, the choirmaster his patience, and Joseph, trying to sing several unequal duets with his oversized, offkey partner, had simply lost his voice.

Jack heard someone whisper, "Look at Jack, the poor old devil, fancy having the guts to come back after last year." He ignored it, determined not to get himself upset about a plastic doll in the same old crib. Reminding the cast that this was their last rehearsal, the vicar said that he was sure that the actual performance would go swimmingly provided the gentlemen of the cast remembered that with all the ladies, angel children and choir trying to get dressed in the tiny vestry, they must follow the practice of other years, using the good offices of the Horse and Harrow porch and bar in which to wait or get into their costumes.

A small lad had been detailed as runner so that the performers could make their entries through the west door of the church on cue.

On Christmas Eve it seemed that the entire population of the village was heading for the church or the Horse and Harrow bar. Mixing with customers who had popped in for a quick one were black-faced kings in cretonne curtains, shepherds in striped dressing gown robes and bed-ticking headdresses. Scorning such make-believe, Jack wore the same outfit he had used to play the chief shepherd from the beginning, his father's billycock hat, his buckskin leggings and his old smock.

Rather than watch his wife's performance as Mary, Joe Gimble had volunteered to serve behind the bar, helped by a pleasant young chap who was acting barman and staying with Tom over Christmas.

As the church organ started the introduction to 'While Shepherds Watched', Jack knew it was his cue to go. Most of the others in the bar seemed to fall in behind him, pausing at the great west door as he walked slowly up the main aisle of the church.

Realising that this year the plump and none-too-youthful Mrs. Gimble and a plastic doll would be waiting by the wide steps of the chancel, he thought it would be easy to control his emotions, but somehow the familiar blue and white costume altered her appearance, making her look thinner. He told himself that it was just a trick of the lights. The routine had become so familiar that he paced his steps to the music almost automatically, the last notes dying as he stood before Joseph and the kneeling figure in blue and white.

"I, a simple shepherd...." he began, saying his words and acting out his part by slowly draping a sheep fleece across one corner of the crib. As he did so, the baby stirred, snuffling as a tiny hand moved and a pair of dark brown eyes opened wide. Completely lost for words and oblivious of his surroundings, he gazed down at the face of his daughter as she had looked at six months old. He lifted the baby, cuddling it close to him as it chuckled and gurgled, knowing that in this strange other world he only had to brush away the unbidden tears and turn his head to see his own beloved wife. 'Mary' moved toward him, touching his arm tremulously and whispering, "Oh, my darling Dad!"

It was no part of the planned performance for 'Mary' to hug a shepherd, or for that shepherd to spend the rest of the evening with the babe cradled in his arms. Under the cover of carols being sung, Ruth and her father spoke of matters that were not in any script. The rest of the nativity play took on a dreamlike sequence and when it was all over, Tom and the young man Jack had seen behind the bar at the Horse and Harrow earlier that evening came over to where he sat with his daughter and grandson in a dim-lit pew.

"Well Jack, my old matey, you have your son-in-law to thank for this reunion. You would never believe the conniving and planning since he wrote to my missus. Joe Gimble's wife, the vicar and half the ruddy village have been in on the secret."

"You don't want to keep that youngster here all night," Tom continued. "Ruth and her husband are staying with us for Christmas. Seeing you won't have made any preparations I don't suppose you have to rush back home so you had better pitch in with us."

Walking back, cradling his sleeping grandson in the sheep fleece, Jack realized that from this moment his home would not have that awful echoing empty silence. As for tonight, he could find no adequate words to express his thanks that the world still contained caring kindly folk who could find room at the inn.

Liza

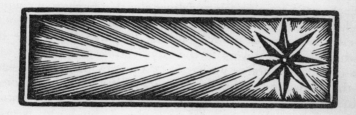

The proportions of Liza's sightless world had become reduced to the width of six painted bricks and encompassed by the cot rails round her hospital bed. Sickened with our own futile inability, we who loved her watched and wept the dry-eyed frozen tears that formed like lumps of ice to block one's throat. All the goblins of Hell seemed sometimes to conspire to torment her tired brain, but in her lucid moments she still retained the ability to create that atmosphere of love and tranquillity that had surrounded her all her life. She, so terribly afflicted, became our comforter, offering us solace in that small-windowed, dark ward that had witnessed the end of so many old dreams.

Knowing what part the hospital building had played in her long life, we were reluctant to leave her when the precious time for visiting was done, lingering at her bedside to clasp the hands that had spent a lifetime caring for our needs. Lifting her blind placid face for a benedictory farewell kiss, she offered comfort in her oft repeated phrase. "Don't fret so, love! Harry came to take me from this place before, and he will come again!"

Liza's Harry was born and raised in a sheep farming community on the coastal marshes, with everyone around him being related by marriage or by birth. At twenty years old, he was tall, dark haired, brown eyed, broad shouldered, and afraid of nothing, the obvious choice when it came to driving the two-horse waggon to the city wool chandler, and haggle the best price for the fleeces he had for sale.

Each year he undertook to deliver a wicker hamper of country produce to an aunt by marriage who had returned to the maze of city back streets to live out her widowed life. Since the journey involved staying in the city overnight, he lodged with this good lady, stabling his horses at a nearby inn, leaving early on the following morning to drive the thirty miles back home.

In the early summer of 1897, Harry set off on his annual journey leaving his home before daybreak, his horses wearing coloured worsted braids and burnished brasses, and he, smart dressed and striding out beside them, walking all the way.

Some two miles from his destination, he stopped at the top of a steep hill to rest his horses in the shade of tall laurels skirting a gravel drive. While the horses munched hay and oats from their nosebags, Harry put iron skidpans to the back wheels of the heavy waggon in preparation for the sharp descent. The city in the valley shimmered in a cauldron of heat haze and smoking chimneys, grey and uninviting. Close by, the shady long green drive framed the mock Gothic edifice of a boarding college for the sons of gentry. Harry imagined that to board there must be like living in a church.

A grey-dressed, thin young woman came limping along the drive as he hung the empty feed bags under the back axle of the waggon. He realised that she was one of the numerous daughters of his widowed aunt's neighbour, and asked if she would walk beside him down into the town. For a while he watched her hobbling along in boots that were plainly torture, then with scant ceremony hoisted Liza up to ride on the footboard of the waggon beside his aunt's wicker hamper. When he teased her that she was about as hefty as a hen robin in mid-winter, and crazy to wear crippling badly-made boots, she retorted that he might have been a few stone lighter if he had grown up knowing what it was like never to have quite enough to eat.

She was one of a family numbering thirteen, having seven younger brothers and sisters, and since her father had died of lockjaw when the youngest was still in swaddling binders, the wage of six pounds every Lady Day and Michaelmas was her contribution toward keeping her family from the workhouse door.

Cursing his bumpkin clumsiness, Harry plodded along in silence watching the pinched shadow of hunger on this pretty young girl's face. When he stopped the horses at the bottom of the hill to unhitch the skidpans, he opened his aunt's hamper to bring out a yeast cake wrapped in a white cloth.

"See if that will stop the mice gnawing at your innards!" he mumbled awkwardly then, as an afterthought, drew out the nosegay of lily of the valley that his grandmother had picked for his widowed aunt, and thrust it into Liza's hand.

Liza munched manfully, not caring now that her monthly half day off had started so late and must end at eight thirty that evening.

"Happen I could walk back here with you tonight then," Harry said, blushing.

"Happen I'll not let you!" Liza retorted, but she did. As Harry strolled with her that summer evening, he knew that he had met no girl to match her gentle beauty and irrepressible sense of humour in all his twenty years.

"Will you bring me a yeast cake and flowers when you come with the wool clip next year Harry?" she asked, smiling as they parted.

"You can't eat flowers!" Harry retorted. "Would a mutton 'fiddle' do instead? Next year when I come, we might do some serious talking." Harry watched her hurry down the drive.

Her thin face haunted him, waking or sleeping, all through the passing seasons. He wrote a letter to her, addressing it to the college, but had no reply. When he set out to take the next shearing to the city chandler, he was determined to find her and ask if he could court her. Again he stopped the horses by the college entrance but now there was no sheltering shade, for the laurels had been cut down. There was no Liza either, but Harry told himself that she only had one half day off every month and it was unlikely that he could be so lucky twice.

When the wool was sold, Harry stood awkwardly in his aunt's over-ornamented parlour and mentioned Liza's name.

"You won't give her my cake or flowers this year my lad! The poor dumb thing has been in the Workhouse since the start of last winter. What that poor girl endured left her witless and numbed her brain."

Stopping just long enough to hear of a timid girl waylaid, attacked and robbed of her half-yearly wages in the college shrubbery, Harry strode to the grim Poor Law Institution on the hill, demanding to see the master or matron of the place, and in a cell-like office the situation was explained. When Liza was found in a distressed state, bruised and bleeding, she dared to accuse some young college gentlemen without a shred of evidence to support her story. This earned her dismissal without references. Because she had no means of support, she could not be released to become a vagrant and an encumbrance on the parish rates.

No responsible citizen could be expected to employ a servant girl who existed in a dream world and had lost the power of speech so, although she was physically healed she had to work in the institution to help pay for her keep.

Demanding to see Liza, Harry found her wearing a drab union flannel smock and cap, and scrubbing a stone floor. If she was thin before, now she was pathetic. Only as he ran forward to lift her from her knees did he realise that he still had his aunt's country hamper on his arm. Her eyes were devoid of hope or expression as he called her name.

Frantic, Harry delved into the hamper trying to make her recall the yeast cake incident of the previous year. That failed to register, then he remembered the flowers that were intended for his aunt. As Liza pressed her face against the lily of the valley, their scent seemed to release some message to her brain. She looked at Harry in wonder and astonishment then, brushing away the tears that were streaming down his face, whispered hoarsely, "Harry love, don't cry." The matron suggested Harry apply to employ Liza formally so as to gain her release. "Employ her!" thundered Harry, "I want to marry her, Liza is going to be my wife! I'll take her out of here today!"

That was not possible. Formalities decreed that the banns of marriage be read for three consecutive Sundays, and only after the service could Harry claim her for his own. Some of his shearing money went to pay for Liza to be moved to the matron's private quarters and given extra nourishment.

Three weeks later Harry drove back to claim his bride, bringing with him a bunch of flowers and a grey silk wedding dress with an eighteen inch waist.

Their wedding was at noon, and by one o'clock Harry and his bride were out of the city, riding in a pony cart between hedgerows heavy with the scent of sweet briar and honeysuckle.

After eight long months of incarceration in a drab grey world, each roadside flower was to Liza a thing of wonder and delight. Good food, fresh air and Harry's gentle love worked wonders, and by harvest time Liza was sufficiently recovered to work beside her husband making bonds for the sheaves of corn he scythed.

They planted a bed of lily of the valley in their garden and thus the pattern of their life together was set. They met setbacks and heartaches, but with sheer hard work and a deep abiding love, built up a farm of their own.

They had a large family, but Liza made quite sure that none of her children ever knew the workhouse fears that had plagued her early life. For many golden years Harry and Liza created a quiet paradise, until men who saw the land as just so many acres of earth, brought their plans, their machines and their concrete mixers to tear the heart out of the fields, forcing Harry and Liza to leave the life they loved.

A few more autumnal years, then as Liza watched her Harry lose the battle against a cancerous scourge of sickness, something deep inside her soul died too. Sick in body, with the precious lamp of sight growing ever dimmer, Liza became so afflicted that she required constant medical attention. She was admitted to the geriatric hospital back in the refurbished old workhouse, and to her sightless muddled mind everything was as she remembered it before.

If the wheel had turned full circle, Liza steadfastly believed that Harry, who took her from this place before, would come for her again. We who loved her took her faith to be the ramblings of a senile brain, but we were utterly mistaken.

It was just an ordinary visit at the time of the year when the lily of the valley still bloomed beside her old back garden fence, and at visiting time one of her beloved children placed a bunch of them in her hands. She fingered the delicate flowers of the posy for a moment, then held them up to her face.

Full of wonderment, the eyes that had been dull and sightless for so long focussed in joyful recognition as an expression of sheer happiness came into her face. With a smile as radiant as a bride, she touched the flowers with her lips, sighing just one word of greeting in her deep contentment. Harry had taken his Liza home.

Liza

The returning dream took me home again
With the song of the years as yet unsung.
I walked by the side of the upright man,
As I did in the days when my heart was young.
Grazing sheep, placid cows, and an old white horse
All turned their heads as they passed him by.
A little black dog with long flapping ears
Looked at him with love and so did I.
We leaned on the gate and surveyed the land
That had known our laughter, toil, and tears,
Then Dad spoke of the bonds we had welded so strong
As we worked side by side in the golden years.
He talked of my Mum, and the ones that I love,
Of the echoing past, and of dreams to be
And he said that life changing and the mirage of death
Could never take this away from me.